READING AND WRITING FOR TODAY'S ADULTS

# Voyager 1

MARY DUNN SIEDOW

New Readers Press

**Advisers to the Series**

Mary Dunn Siedow
Linda Thistlethwaite

**Reviewer**

Sondra Luebke

**Acknowledgments**

Fehler, Gene. "Winner" from CENTER FIELD GRASSES: POEMS FROM BASEBALL © 1991 Gene Fehler, by permission of McFarland & Company, Inc., Publishers, Jefferson, NC 28640.

"Dreams" from THE COLLECTED POEMS OF LANGSTON HUGHES by Langston Hughes, edited by Arnold Rampersad with David Roessel, Associate Editor, copyright © 1994 by the Estate of Langston Hughes. Used by permission of Alfred A. Knopf, a division of Random House, Inc.

Kaufman, Shirley. "The Arch" from WORDS ON THE PAGE, THE WORLD IN YOUR HANDS, BOOK ONE published by HarperCollins. Reprinted by permission of the author.

Marsh, Elizabeth. "Can't" from THE READING TEACHER, May 1981. Reprinted by permission of the International Reading Association.

Mosack, Dan. "My Best Friend" from TO OPEN YOUR MIND, Vol. 5, No. 1, Winter 1995. Reprinted by permission.

Toni, "A Special Friend." Reprinted by permission from NEED I SAY MORE, Vol. III, No.2 (Summer 1990), a publication of the Publishing for Literacy Project, jointly sponsored by the Public Library of Brookline (MA) and the Adult Literacy Resource Institute of Roxbury Community College and the University of Massachusetts/Boston.

Voyager: Reading and Writing for Today's Adults
ISBN 978-1-56420-910-8


New Readers Press
ProLiteracy's Publishing Division
104 Marcellus Street, Syracuse, New York 13204
www.newreaderspress.com



Printed in the United States of America
9 8 7

Proceeds from the sale of New Readers Press materials support professional development, training, and technical assistance programs of ProLiteracy that benefit local literacy programs in the U.S. and around the globe.

**Developmental Editor:** Terrie Lipke
**Creative Director:** Andrea Woodbury
**Developer:** Learning Unlimited, Oak Park, IL
**Production Specialist:** Maryellen Casey
**Art and Design Supervisor:** James P. Wallace
**Illustrations:** Judy Love and Drew Rose, represented by Wilkinson Studios, Inc.
**Cover Design:** James P. Wallace

ProLiteracy and New Readers Press are not owned or sponsored by Voyager Expanded Learning, Inc.

# Contents

We all have hopes and dreams. Before you start Unit 1, think about your hopes and dreams. What do you want in life? How will you make your dreams come true?

Lesson 1

# A Class of Hopes

**Learning Goals**
**Strategy:** Use your experience to help you understand what you read
**Reading:** Read a story
**Skill:** Sequence events
**Writing:** Make a list
**Word Work:** Short vowels (*a*, *e*, *i*, *o*, *u*)

Trabajo

## Before You Read

"A Class of Hopes" is a story about adults who are learning to read better. Learning to read will help them make their dreams come true.

**1.** Talk about the things adults need to read.
Why did you decide to improve your reading?
What do you hope will happen when you can read better?

**2.** ✓Check the sentences that are true for you. Write two more reasons why you want to learn to read better.

I want to read

_____ the newspaper.

_____ for my job.

_____ to help my children with their homework.

______________________________________________

______________________________________________

## Key Words

- Jan goes to school.
- Ken wants to learn to read better.
- Ken hopes to read stories to his son.
- Brad wants to go to college.

## As You Read

People in this story hope to have better lives. As you read, think about their lives. What are they doing to help them make their dreams come true?

# A Class of Hopes

Ken goes to school. He wants to learn to read. He wants to read stories to his son, Russ.

Jan goes to school, too. She wants to read better. She hopes to work in a shop. She has to read to work in a shop.

Brad has a job. He cuts grass. But he wants a better job. He hopes to go to college, too. Brad has to read well to go to college.

Ken, Jan, and Brad all hope for better lives. They work hard. They know that they must learn to read better.

## After You Read

Discuss these questions.

1. Why does Ken want to read better? Why does Jan want to read better? Why does Brad want to read better?
2. What are Ken, Jan, and Brad doing to make their dreams come true?
3. How will reading better help you? What changes will reading better make in your life?

## Think About It: Sequence Events

**Sequence** is the order in which things happen.

First your alarm clock rings.

Then you get up.

Last you get dressed.

## Practice

**A. Sequence words** Read the sequence words in the box.

| First | Then | Last |
|---|---|---|

**B.** Look at the pictures. Number them in order. Copy the word from the box under the right picture.

1

First

**C.** Read the sentences. Number them in order. Then copy each sentence next to the right picture.

____ Ken learns to read and write better.

1 Ken goes to class.

____ Ken reads stories to Russ.

**1.** First Ken goes to class.

**2.** Then ______________________

______________________

**3.** Last ______________________

______________________

**D.** Read the sentences. Number them in order. Copy them in the right order.

____ Jan learns to read better. First Jan hopes for a better life.

____ Jan gets a job in a shop. Then ______________________

1 Jan hopes for a better life. Last ______________________

## Write About It: Make a List

**A. Brad's Plan** In "A Class of Hopes," Ken, Jan, and Brad have special dreams. Brad wants a better job. He makes a plan. Brad's plan has five steps. Read his plan.

**Brad's Plan**

1. Learn to read and write better.
2. Take a GED class.
3. Get my GED.
4. Go to college.
5. Get a better job.

**B.** Brad's plan is a list. Each step has its own line. Copy Brad's plan onto the lines below. Be sure each step starts on a new line.

**Brad's Plan**

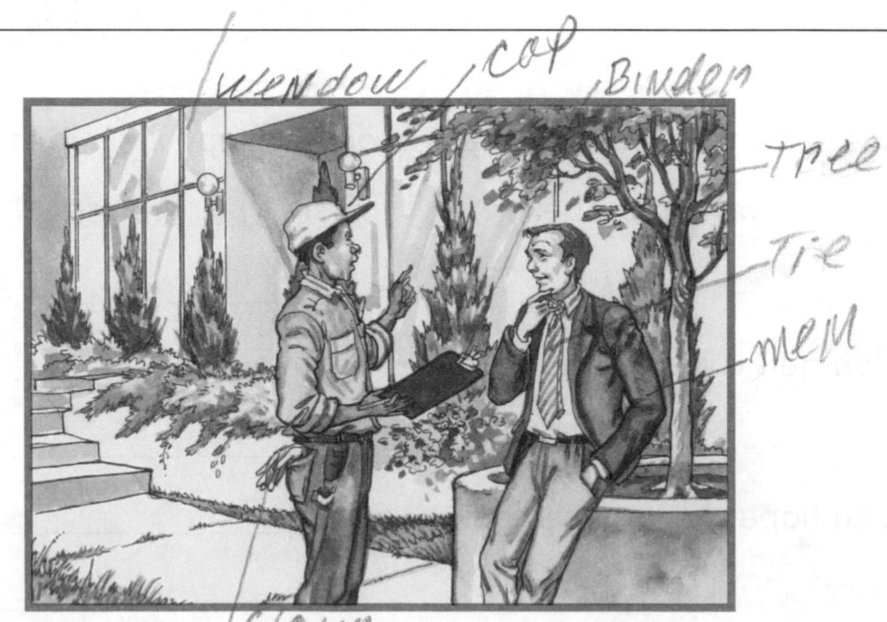

**C. My Plan** Now write your own plan. Start by finishing #1.

**1.** Write your dream on the line.

My dream is ______________________________

______________________________

**2.** What will you do to make your dream come true?
Write a list of steps. Number them in order.

**My Plan**

___ ______________________________

___ ______________________________

___ ______________________________

___ ______________________________

___ ______________________________

**3.** Check your list. Be sure the steps are numbered in the right order.
Then rewrite your plan in the right order.

**My Plan**

___ ______________________________

___ ______________________________

___ ______________________________

___ ______________________________

___ ______________________________

## Word work: Short vowels (*a, e, i, o, u*)

**A.** The words below have short vowel sounds. Read the words. Listen to the vowel sounds.

| a | e | i | o | u |
|---|---|---|---|---|
| Jan | Ken | it | on | us |
| has | get | in | job | but |
| Brad | then | big | lot | much |
| plan | well | did | shop | must |
| class | better | this | college | Russ |

**B.** Say the two words under each picture. Pick the word that says what you see. Then write it on the line.

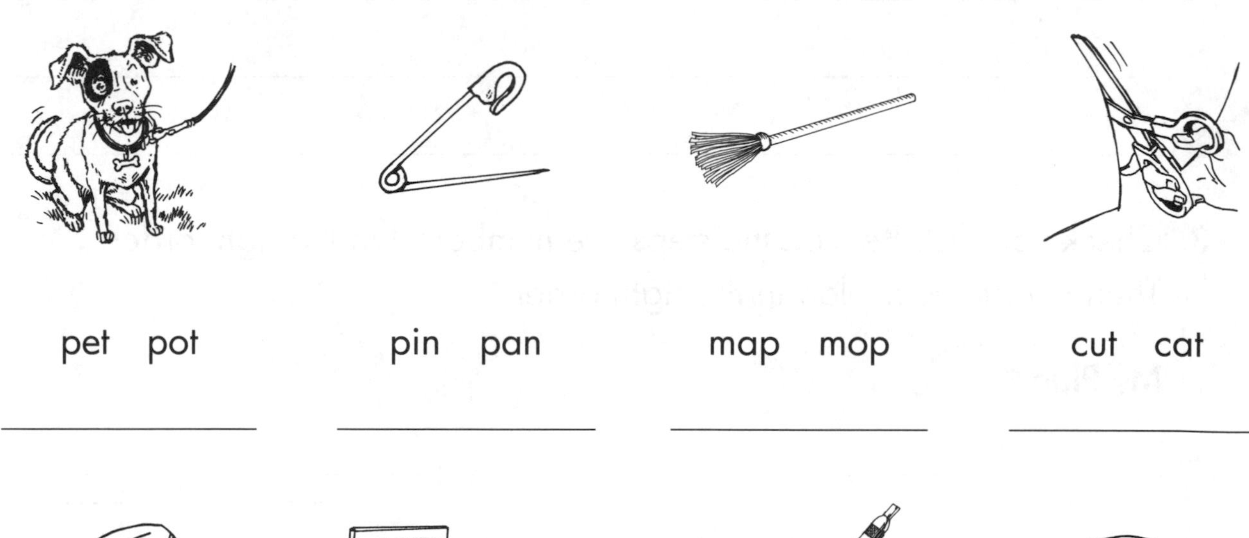

pet pot ______ pin pan ______ map mop ______ cut cat ______

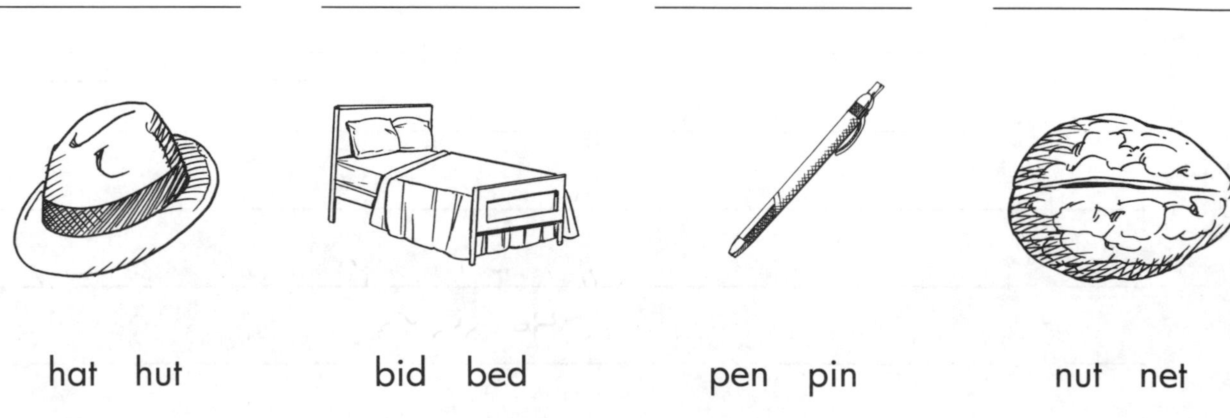

hat hut ______ bid bed ______ pen pin ______ nut net ______

**C.** Write vowels in the blanks to make words. The first group is done for you.

| a | e | i | o | u |
|---|---|---|---|---|

| | | | |
|---|---|---|---|
| b _a_ d | h ____ m | b ____ t | l ____ ck |
| b _e_ d | h ____ m | b ____ t | l ____ ck |
| b _i_ d | h ____ m | b ____ t | l ____ ck |
| b _u_ d | h ____ m | b ____ t | l ____ ck |

**D. Word Families** A **word family** is a group of words that share the same set of letters. Words in a family rhyme, too. Word families help you read many new words. Read the words. Write other words you know in each family on the lines.

| -ad | -en | -id | -ot | -un |
|---|---|---|---|---|
| bad | den | bid | cot | bun |
| dad | hen | did | hot | fun |
| had | Ken | lid | jot | run |
| glad | then | slid | slot | stun |
| ________ | ________ | ________ | ________ | ________ |
| ________ | ________ | ________ | ________ | ________ |
| ________ | ________ | ________ | ________ | ________ |

**Update on "A Class of Dreams"** It is a few years later. Ken's son, Russ, is in school. He needs help with his homework. He asks Ken for help. What do you think happens?

Lesson 2

AT = EN Y POR

TO = para

# A New Life

**Learning Goals**

**Strategy:** Use what you know to understand what you read

**Reading:** Read a story

**Skill:** Identify cause and effect

**Writing:** Write a poem

**Word Work:** Initial consonant blends (*br, cl, gr, pl, st*)

## Before You Read

"A New Life" is a story about a man who came to the U.S. from Mexico. Before you read, answer these questions.

**1.** Think of a person who was born in another country. Write about the person here.

Name: is MARTA LEDESMA

Country: FREEPORT

Language: English

**2.** Talk about why people move to new countries. ✓Check the reasons you think people come to the U.S. Write another reason.

✓ to get a better job

✓ to be with family

____ to be with friends

____ to get married

____ to feel more safe

____________

## Key Words

- Sal is from <u>Mexico</u>.
- He learned <u>English</u>.
- Sal <u>missed</u> his <u>family</u>.
- He went to class at <u>night</u>.

## As You Read

As you read, think about Sal's dreams. What dreams does he have?

# A New Life

Sal Castro was born in Mexico. He spent 25 years there. But Sal dreamed of a better life. He came to Dallas, Texas, to make that dream come true.

Life in the U.S. was hard for Sal. He missed his family. He worked hard each day. He went to class at night. Sal learned English. He got a better job.

Now Sal has a new dream. He plans to visit his family in Mexico. He will give them gifts. He will tell them about his new life. Sal will be glad to see his family.

## After You Read

Retell the story about Sal. Here are some ways to start.

1. Sal comes from
2. Sal came to Texas because
3. Each day Sal . . .
4. He learned . . .
5. Sal's new dream is . . .

## Think About It: Identify Cause and Effect

A **cause** is what makes something happen. An effect is what happens.

**Cause** **Effect**

## Practice

**A. Match** Write the letter of the correct effect next to the cause.

**Cause** **Effect**

1. C

2. A

3. b

a.

b.

c.

**B.** Read the **Effect** sentence. Look at the picture. ✓ Check the sentence that tells the **Cause.** The first one is done for you.

1\. 

**Effect** Sal came to Texas.

**Cause** (1) __✓__ He was born in Mexico.

(2) __✓__ He wanted a better life.

2\. 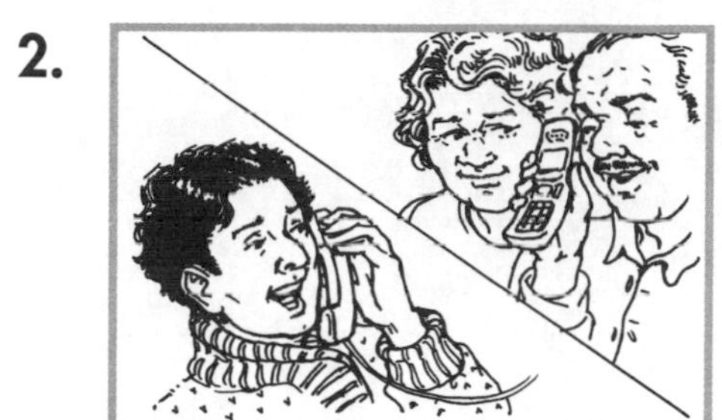

**Effect** Sal calls his family on the phone.

**Cause** (1) __✓__ He misses his family.

(2) ____ He works hard.

3\. 

**Effect** Sal went to class at night.

**Cause** (1) __✓__ He wanted a better job.

(2) ____ He wanted to visit his family.

**C.** Write a sentence that tells what is happening in the picture (effect). Then write a sentence that tells what you think made it happen (cause).

**Effect** Sal is gradvating From The Enlesh course

**Cause** He will get a bette Job

## Write About It: Write a Poem

### Sal's Poem

Sal wrote this poem in class. Read Sal's poem.

Sal
Mexican, brave, hardworking, hopeful
Son of Ben and Bella
Brother of Carmen, Victor, and Martin
Who feels glad to be here
Who likes sunny days
Who needs family, friends, and work
Who lives in Dallas, Texas
Castro

What details does the poem give about Sal? Discuss Sal's poem.

### My Poem

**A.** Think about Sal's poem. Write a poem about yourself. Write a draft here.

Your first name: MARTHA

Four words that tell about you: DOMINICAN, WERKER, brave FRIENDLY

Son or daughter of: CRISTINA and Luis

Brother, sister, or friend of: ANTONIO EDI SACARIA JERMAN

Who feels: HAPPY WITH LIFE

Who likes: GO TO SHOPING

Who needs: CASH MONEY

Who lives in: FREEPORT

Your last name: LEDESMA

**B.** Look at the draft of your poem. Do these two steps:

____ **1.** Change any words you want to change.

____ **2.** Have another reader read your poem. Can he or she understand it? If not, make any changes you need.

**C.** Copy the final draft of your poem here.

________________________________________

________________________________________

________________________________________

________________________________________

Who feels ________________________________

Who likes ________________________________

Who needs ________________________________

Who lives in ______________________________

________________________________________

## Word Work: Initial Consonant Blends (*br, cl, gr, pl, st*)

**A.** Read the words in each list. Can you hear two sounds in the beginning blends?

| **br** | **cl** | **gr** | **pl** | **st** |
|---|---|---|---|---|
| brave | clam | grab | plan | stop |
| bring | clip | grill | plant | star |
| broom | club | grin | plate | state |
| brush | class | grass | plug | story |
| brother | clock | grand | plum | stand |

**B.** Read the two words under each picture. Pick the word that says what you see. Then write it on the line.

clock crock

clock

stop shop

stop

class grass

grass

groom broom

broom

scar star

star

plant grant

plant

crush brush

brush

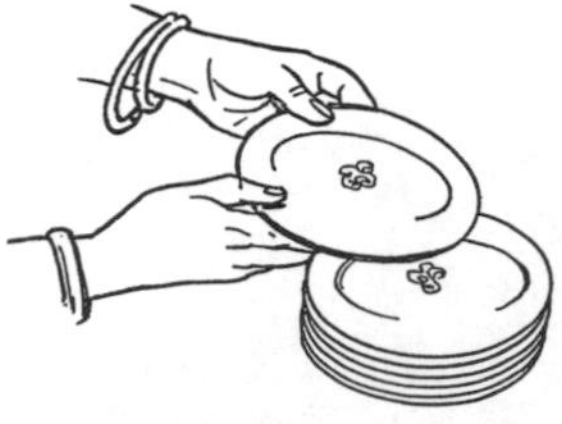

plate late

plate

**C. Word Families** Read the words in these word families. Write other words you know in each family on the lines.

| -an | -ass | -ing | -op | -ub |
|---|---|---|---|---|
| man | pass | ring | mop | rub |
| bran | brass | bring | top | club |
| clan | class | cling | plop | grub |
| plan | grass | sting | stop | stub |
| WOMON | ______ | reading | SHOP | NUb |

**D.** Pick the right word for each sentence. Write it on the line.

**1.** ___Sal___ came to the U.S. from Mexico.
(Pal, Sal)

**2.** Sal went to ___class___ at night.
(class, grass)

**3.** Sal lives in the ___State___ of Texas.
(plate, state)

**4.** Sal ___PlaNS___ to visit his family.
(clans, plans)

**5.** He will be ___glad___ to see his family.
(glad, grad)

**Update on "A New Life"** Sal has worked hard. He knows English now. He has a better job. Now he can send money home. His brother wants to come to the U.S., too. He will live with Sal. What do you think will happen?

I Think your brother will have to learn English to be able to have a good Jab too and Sal will suppt you financiall so That iT goes ahead

Lesson 3

# Dreams

**Learning Goals**
**Strategy:** Picture what you read
**Reading:** Read a poem
**Skill:** Understand the main idea
**Writing:** Write a poem
**Word Work:** Final consonant blends (*ft, ld, mp, nt, st*)

## Before You Read

Langston Hughes is a famous African American poet. In this lesson you will read his poem "Dreams." This poem tells us what life is like without hopes and dreams.

1. Why are your hopes and dreams important to you?

   becaus That is is The reason of Tha Future

2. What can happen to people when they lose their hopes and dreams?

   Feel dePressed

3. What feelings or pictures come to mind when you think about losing your hopes and dreams?

   a dark picture come to MY mind

## Key Words

- Hold fast means to hold on.
- The broken-winged bird cannot fly.
- No plants can grow in a barren field.

tara

I Feel = comotecinte



## As You Read

In "Dreams," Langston Hughes tells us not to let hopes and dreams die. As you read, what pictures do you see in your mind?

# Dreams

Langston Hughes

Hold fast to dreams
For if dreams die
Life is a broken-winged bird
That cannot fly.

Hold fast to dreams
For when dreams go
Life is a barren field
Frozen with snow.

## After You Read

Discuss these questions.

1. How do you feel after reading this poem?
2. Look at lines 1 and 5. What advice does Hughes give in these lines?
3. Picture a "broken-winged bird." The poet says that a life without dreams is a broken-winged bird. What does he mean?
4. Picture a "barren field." The poet says that a life without dreams is a barren field. What does he mean?
5. Re-read the poem. This time, how does the poem make you feel?

## Think About It: Understand the Main Idea

The main idea of a poem is its most important message. Read "Dreams" once more. The main message of the poem is this:

Hold on to your dreams.

Poets often use words to create pictures, or images, that carry their message. In "Dreams," each stanza, or group of lines, has a different image of a life without dreams. The image in the first stanza is:

. . . if dreams die
Life is a broken-winged bird
That cannot fly.

This is one image of a life without dreams.

## Practice

1. What image of a life without dreams does Hughes use in the second stanza? Write it here.

_______________________________________________

2. Picture the "broken-winged bird" and the "barren field" in your mind. What other words can you think of to describe them?

_______________________________________________

3. "Dreams" tells us what happens if we let go of our dreams:

   - Life is a broken-winged bird that cannot fly.
   - Life is a barren field frozen with snow.

   What do you think happens if we hold on to our dreams?

_______________________________________________

_______________________________________________

## Write About It: Write a Poem

Read these poems. Talk about how they are different and how they are alike.

**Dreams**

Hold fast to dreams
For if dreams die
Life is a broken-winged bird
That cannot fly.

Hold fast to dreams
For when dreams go
Life is a barren field
Frozen with snow.

**Let Go**

Let go of hate
For if hate dies
Life is a soaring bird
That owns the sky.

Let go of fear
For when fears pass
Life is a green field
Alive with grass.

**A.** Read the poem "Let Go" again. Think of words you can change in the poem.

**B.** Write your new poem below.

**Let Go**

Let go of ______________________________

For if ______________________________

Life is ______________________________

That ______________________________

Let go of ______________________________

For when ______________________________

Life is ______________________________

Alive ______________________________

## Word Work: Final Consonant Blends (*ft, ld, mp, nt, st*)

**A.** Read the words in each list. Can you hear two sounds in the ending blends?

| ft | ld | mp | nt | st |
|---|---|---|---|---|
| gift | old | lamp | cent | best |
| left | hold | pump | pint | cost |
| lift | child | clump | went | fast |
| raft | field | stamp | grant | must |

**B.** Read the two words under each picture. Pick the word that says what you see. Then write it on the line.

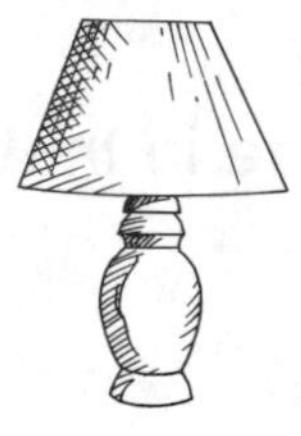

lamp land

________________

chill child

________________

best bent

________________

gift girl

________________

bump pump

________________

field film

________________

send cent

________________

stamp stand

________________

**C. Word Families** Read the words in these word families. Write another word you know in each family on the lines.

| -amp | -est | -old | -ift | -ump |
|---|---|---|---|---|
| lamp | best | cold | gift | bump |
| ramp | test | hold | drift | pump |
| clamp | chest | sold | shift | plump |
| stamp | guest | scold | swift | stump |
| __________ | __________ | __________ | __________ | __________ |

**D. Crossword Puzzle** Fill in the missing letters to complete the puzzle with words from the Word List.

**WORD LIST**

BARREN
BROKEN
CHEST
CLAMP
FAST
FIELD
HOLD
LEFT
NOW
OWN
STAMP
SWIFT
TENT
WENT
WINGED

# Review

## Reading Review

### Dreams

In this unit, we learned about some hopes and dreams. Ken, Jan, and Brad want to read better. They go to class to make their dreams come true. Sal wanted a better life. He came to Texas to make this dream come true.

Dreams mean a lot to Ken, Jan, Brad, and Sal. They work hard to make their dreams come true.

Choose the best answer to each question.

**1.** Which sentence best tells the main idea of "Dreams"?

Dream (1) In this unit, we learned about some hopes and dreams.

____ (2) Ken, Jan, and Brad want to read better.

____ (3) Sal wanted a better life.

**2. Effect:** Ken, Jan, and Brad go to class.
What is the cause?

____ (1) They want to read better.

____ (2) They want to have dreams.

**3. Effect:** Sal came to Texas.
What is the cause?

____ (1) He learned English.

____ (2) He wanted a better life.

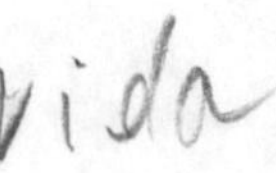

I drINK a lOT OF waTer

## Word Work Review

Pick the right word. Write it on the line.

1. Ken goes to reading class.
   (class, grass)

2. He has a son named Russ.
   (his, has)

3. Jan hopes to work in a Shop.
   (stop, shop)

4. Brad dreams about a better JOb.
   (jab, job)

5. Sal has a new PlaN.
   (plan, plant)

6. We need to hold on to our dreams.
   (host, hold)

7. Dreams can make us do our best.
   (bent, best)

## Write About It

**Topic:** What is your dream? What are you doing to make it come true?

I waNT TO SPeaK eNGLISH

**Prewrite** Think about the topic questions. List some ideas.

**Write** Pick your best ideas. Write about your dream.

**Revise** Look at your sentences again. Change any words you want to change. Have someone read your writing. Can he or she understand it?

**Edit** Find and correct mistakes in your writing. See page 112.

**Final Draft** Make a final copy to keep and share.

Not all heroes are big and strong. Not all heroes fight in a war. Not all heroes save a life. Heroes are brave. We admire heroes. Before you start Unit 2, think about heroes. What makes a person a hero? Who are some heroes you admire?

Lesson 4

# A Bus Ride

**Learning Goals**

**Strategy:** Use what you know to understand what you read
**Readings:** Read about two real-life heroes
**Skill:** Make predictions
**Writing:** Write about what you read
**Word Work:** Long *a* and long *i*

## Before You Read

"A Bus Ride" is about a woman who became a real-life hero. Before you read, answer these questions.

1. Look at the title of the reading on page 29. Look at the picture. What do you think the reading may be about? Write your prediction here.

_______________________________________________

_______________________________________________

2. Discuss what you know about the U.S. civil rights movement of the 1950s and 1960s.
3. Discuss the kinds of laws that were changed by the civil rights movement.

## Key Words

- Alabama had an unfair law.
- Rosa Parks paid her fare to ride the bus.
- Rosa Parks was arrested.
- Now people can sit anywhere on a bus.
- Cesar Chavez formed a union for farm workers.

## As You Read

As you read, think about what Rosa Parks did. Why is she a hero?

© Bettmann/CORBIS

# A Bus Ride

In 1955 Rosa Parks took a bus ride. That ride changed her life. It changed the law, too.

Alabama had an unfair law. The law said that white people could sit anywhere on a bus. But black people had to sit in the back of the bus.

One day Rosa Parks got on a bus. She paid her fare. She sat down. But a white man wanted her seat. Ms. Parks did not move. She did not think the law was fair.

Rosa Parks broke the law. She was arrested. Many people heard about Ms. Parks. Black people were mad. They didn't ride the buses. They didn't ride for 381 days.

At last the law was changed. Now people can have any seat on the bus. Rosa Parks took a stand. She helped to change the way people live.

## After You Read

**A.** Tell about Rosa Parks's bus ride. Here are some ways to start.

1. First Rosa Parks paid . . .
2. A white man wanted . . .
3. Ms. Parks did not . . .
4. She was . . .

**B.** Discuss why Rosa Parks is a hero.

## Think About It: Make Predictions

When you **predict,** you try to figure out what a reading will be about. To predict what a reading will be about, use these clues:

- the title
- pictures

On page 28 you made a prediction about the reading. Copy it here.

____________________________________________________________

____________________________________________________________

How did your prediction match the reading? How did it not match?

____________________________________________________________

____________________________________________________________

## Practice

**A.** Read each title and look at each picture. ✓Check the prediction that can be made.

**1.** 

**Title:** Learning to Cook

**Prediction:** (1) ____ The man will read a cookbook.

(2) ____ The man will learn to cook dinner.

**2.** 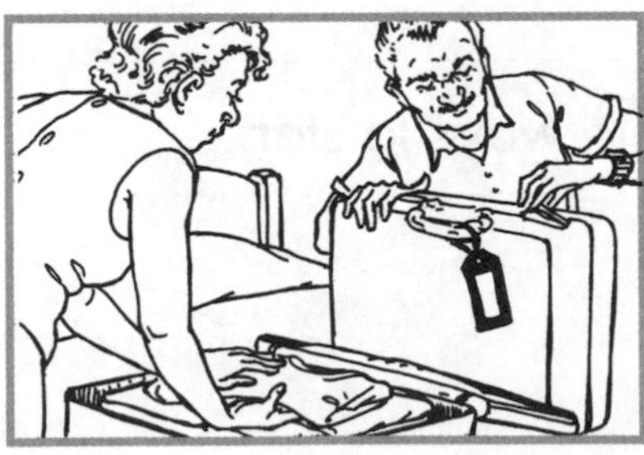

**Title:** Mexico in May

**Prediction:** (1) ____ They will take a trip to Mexico.

(2) ____ They will take a trip to Dallas.

**B.** Read each title and look at each picture. Predict what may happen. Write your prediction.

**1.** 

**Title:** Jan's New Job

**Prediction:** ______________________________

______________________________

**2.** 

**Title:** Brad Moves On

**Prediction:** ______________________________

______________________________

**3.** 

**Title:** Sal Takes a Trip

**Prediction:** ______________________________

______________________________

**C.** Look at the picture on page 32. Read the title. What do you think the article will be about? Write your prediction here.

**Prediction:** ______________________________

______________________________

## Write About It: Write About What You Read

**A.** Read this article about another real-life hero.

### A Hero to Farm Workers

Cesar Chavez was an everyday hero. He was a farm worker in California. He moved from farm to farm. He worked very hard. But he made almost no money. So he started a union.

The union is called the United Farm Workers. The union helps farm workers get more money.

Cesar Chavez gave farm workers hope for a better life. His work made him a hero.

Courtesy of the Library of Congress, Prints and Photographs Division.

**B.** Talk about Cesar Chavez and the United Farm Workers.

**C.** Write about Cesar Chavez in your own words. Here are some words to help you start.

Cesar Chavez was ______________________________

He worked ______________________________

He started ______________________________

He helped ______________________________

He gave farm workers ______________________________

I think he ______________________________

## Word Work: Long *a* and Long *i*

**A.** ***a-e, ai,* and *ay* = Long *a*** The long *a* sounds like the *a* in *name*. Look at the words below. Most words with these letter combinations have a long *a* sound. Read the words.

| a-e | ai | ay |
|---|---|---|
| date | paid | day |
| fare | wait | play |
| gave | rain | stay |
| brave | fair | today |
| plane | sail | maybe |

**B.** Read the word pairs. Underline the word with the long *a* sound.

ran rain

______________

cap cape

______________

sail Sal

______________

plan plane

______________

**C.** Read the word pairs. Underline the word with the long *a* sound.

| | | | |
|---|---|---|---|
| **1.** hat hate | tap tape | made mad | Jan Jane |
| **2.** rain ran | pan pain | pad paid | main man |

**D.** Look at the words you underlined in **C.** Talk about the patterns you see. Fill in the blanks in the patterns below.

**1.** Most words that end in *a* + consonant + silent ______________ have a long *a* sound.

**2.** Most words with *ai* have a ______________ *a* sound.

**E.** ***i–e* and *igh* = Long *i*** The long *i* sounds like *i* in *ride*. Look at the words below. Most words with these letter combinations have a long *i* sound. Read the words.

| i–e | i–e | igh |
|---|---|---|
| life | like | high |
| ride | time | might |
| white | alive | night |
| write | admire | tight |

**F.** Read the word pairs. Underline the word with the long *i* sound. Then write it on the line.

**1.** ride rid ____________________

**2.** bite bit ____________________

**3.** sit sight ____________________

**4.** dim dime ____________________

**5.** fit fight ____________________

**6.** fine fin ____________________

**7.** spin spine ____________________

**8.** ripe rip ____________________

**G.** Look at the words you underlined. Talk about the patterns you see. Fill in the blanks in the patterns below.

**1.** Most words that end in *i* + consonant + silent ____________________ have a long *i* sound.

**2.** Most words with *igh* have a ____________________ *i* sound.

**H.** Sometimes *live* has a short *i* sound. Sometimes it has a long *i* sound. Read the sentences. ✓Check the ones with a long *i* sound for *live*.

_____ **1.** Sal came to live in Texas.

_____ **2.** Sal lived in Mexico.

_____ **3.** Dreams can change lives.

_____ **4.** Rosa Parks lived in Alabama.

**I. Word Families** Read the words in these word families. Write other words you know in each family on the lines.

| -ail | -ain | -ake | -ace | -ame |
|---|---|---|---|---|
| fail | main | make | face | came |
| mail | rain | rake | lace | name |
| nail | brain | shake | brace | blame |
| tail | grain | snake | grace | flame |
| ________ | ________ | ________ | ________ | ________ |

| -ice | -ine | -ite | -ight | -ind |
|---|---|---|---|---|
| mice | fine | bite | night | bind |
| nice | line | kite | right | find |
| price | mine | unite | tight | kind |
| twice | shine | write | bright | grind |
| ________ | ________ | ________ | ________ | ________ |

**J. Practice** Fill in the missing words in the sentences. Choose from the box.

| admire | life | ride | right | white |
|---|---|---|---|---|

1. Rosa Parks took a bus ______________.
2. A ______________ man wanted her seat.
3. She did not think it was ______________.
4. The bus ride changed her ______________.
5. Many people ______________ Rosa Parks.

**Update on "A Bus Ride"** Rosa Parks worked as a tailor until 1965. Then she worked for a congressman. She retired in 1988. She died in 2005 at the age of 92. In honor of the stand she took, she is called the "Mother of the Civil Rights Movement."

Lesson 5

# Neighbor Saves Family

**Learning Goals**
**Strategy:** Picture what you read
**Reading:** Read a news article
**Skill:** Find details
**Writing:** Write about a person you interview
**Word Work:** long *e* and long *y*

## Before You Read

"Neighbor Saves Family" is a news article about a house fire. Before you read the article, answer these questions.

1. Picture a house fire in your mind. Talk about the pictures that come to mind. What people do you see? What are they doing?
2. What words do you know that describe a hero? Write them here.

   __________ __________ __________

3. What everyday heroes do you know?

   ______________________________

   ______________________________

## Key Words

- Steve Meehan helped his neighbor.
- He was already helping.
- The cause of the fire is not known.
- The family was in danger.
- Today Pete retires from his job.

## As You Read

In this story, Steve Meehan is called a hero. As you read, picture Steve's actions in your mind.

### Neighbor Saves Family by Gene Miles

There was a house fire last night. The house was at 5 Beach Street. Steve Meehan, a neighbor, called 911. Then he ran to help Ms. Yee and her baby.

A fire fighter said, "We got to Beach Street fast. But Mr. Meehan was faster. He was already helping. He got Ms. Yee and her baby out the first-floor window. We made sure they were O.K. Then we put out the fire."

Ms. Yee and her baby are fine. "Steve is very brave," Ms. Yee said. "He saved our lives. He's our hero."

The cause of the fire is not known.

## After You Read

**A.** Read the story out loud.

**B.** Discuss these questions.

1. What did you picture in your mind as you read the article?
2. How did Steve get his neighbors out of the house?
3. Why did Ms. Yee call Steve a hero?
4. Steve's neighbors needed help. He did not stop to think about the danger. Do you think all heroes face danger? Are there other kinds of heroes?

## Think About It: Find Details

The facts in a news story are details. Details give us important information. Can you remember details from "Neighbor Saves Family"?

**A.** ✓Check **True** if the detail matches the story. Check **False** if it does not match.

| True | False | |
|---|---|---|
| ____ | ✓ | **1.** The house was at 9 Beach Street. |
| ____ | ____ | **2.** Steve Meehan called 911. |
| ____ | ____ | **3.** The Yee family got out the back door. |
| ____ | ____ | **4.** Fire fighters put the fire out. |
| ____ | ____ | **5.** Ms. Yee said Steve is a hero. |

**B.** Complete each sentence. Use details from "Neighbor Saves Family."

**1.** There was a house fire at ____________________

**2.** Steve Meehan ran to help ____________________

**3.** He got them out the ____________________

**4.** The ____________________ made sure that the Yees were OK.

**5.** Ms. Yee and her baby are ____________________

**6.** Ms. Yee said that Steve is very ____________________

## Practice

**A.** Read this story.

### Fire Fighter Retires by Gene Miles

PETE GREELEY

Pete Greeley was a fire fighter for 25 years. He put out his last fire on Friday. Today he retires.

"Every fire can put people in danger," he said. "A family was in danger. We were lucky that the fire at 5 Beach Street was easy to put out."

Pete has won many prizes and medals. He is a brave man. But Pete doesn't think he is a hero. "I just do my job. I am a fire fighter," he said.

**B.** Complete each sentence. Use details from "Fire Fighter Retires."

**1.** ________________ was a fire fighter for 25 years.

**2.** Pete put out his last fire ________________.

**3.** Pete retires ________________.

**4.** Pete has won many ________________.

**5.** Pete is a ________________ man.

## Write About It: Write About a Person You Interview

Reporters ask questions to get the facts right. These are some of the questions they ask.

**Who?** **What?** **Where?** **When?** **Why?**

| Reporters ask | When they want to know |
|---|---|
| Who? | about people |
| What? | what happened |
| Where? | the place |
| When? | the time, day, week, month, or year |
| Why? | the cause |

**A.** There are many facts in "Neighbor Saves Family." You have to ask questions to get the facts. Match the question to the correct answer.

| | | |
|---|---|---|
| b **1.** Who was a hero? | | **a.** The Yees had a house fire. |
| ____ **2.** What happened? | ✓ | **b.** Steve Meehan |
| ____ **3.** Where was the fire? | | **c.** It is not known. |
| ____ **4.** When was the fire? | | **d.** at 5 Beach Street |
| ____ **5.** Why did the fire start? | | **e.** last night |

**B.** Use a word from the box to complete each question below. Some words may be used more than once. Then interview a partner. Write your partner's answers in the blanks.

| Who | What | Where | When | Why |
|---|---|---|---|---|

| Questions | My partner's answers |
|---|---|
| **1.** ______________ is your name? | ______________ |
| **2.** ______________ were you born? | ______________ |
| **3.** ______________ do you live? | ______________ |
| **4.** ______________ do you like to do? | ______________ |
| **5.** ______________ work do you do? | ______________ |

Now write your own question. Ask your partner this, too.

**6.** ______________________________________________

______________________________________________

**C.** Write about your partner. Use the facts you learned. Then read your writing aloud.

**1.** My partner's name is ______________________

**2.** ______________ was born ______________________
(partner's name)

**3.** ______________ lives ______________________

**4.** ______________ likes to ______________________

**5.** ______________ works ______________________

**6.** ______________________________________________

## Word Work: Long *e* and Long *y*

**A. *e, ee,* and *e–e* = Long *e*** Long *e* sounds like *e* in *be*. Look at the words below. Most words with these letters have a long *e* sound. Read the words.

| e | ee | e–e |
|---|---|---|
| be | need | Pete |
| he | week | Steve |
| me | green | these |
| she | street | complete |

**B. The Letters *ea*** Look at the words below. The letters *ea* have three different sounds. Read the words.

| **ea** as in **each** | **ea** as in **head** | **ea** as in **great** |
|---|---|---|
| easy | bread | break |
| reach | ahead | steak |
| year | already | greatly |
| dream | breakfast | outbreak |

**Tip** When you see a new word with *ea*, first try *ea* as in *each* (long *e*). Then, if you don't hear a word you know, try *ea* as in *head* (short *e*). Last try *ea* as in *great* (long *a*).

**C.** Sometimes *read* has a long e sound. Sometimes it has a short e sound. The sound depends on the sentence. Read the sentences. ✓Check the ones with a long e sound for *read*.

____ **1.** Did you read the story in the newspaper?

____ **2.** Steve read about the house fire.

____ **3.** Ken reads to Russ every night.

____ **4.** I read about the fire last night.

**D. *y* as a Long Vowel** The letter *y* can sound like long *i* as in *my* or like long *e* as in *any*. Read the words.

| **y** as in **my** | **y** as in **any** |
|---|---|
| by | city |
| fly | many |
| why | story |
| myself | family |

## Practice

**E.** Finish the sentences. Use the words in the box.

> **easy**
> **Why**
> **bravery**

1. ________________ do we admire heroes?
2. We admire their ________________.
3. It is not ________________ to be a hero.

**F.** Read these words. Cross out the word in each row that does not have a long vowel sound. The first one is done for you.

| | | | |
|---|---|---|---|
| **1.** we | weed | week | ~~web~~ |
| **2.** peek | pet | peel | Pete |
| **3.** bet | bee | be | by |
| **4.** feet | feel | fee | fed |
| **5.** heed | head | he | heel |
| **6.** flee | fly | fleet | flat |

**Update on "Neighbor Saves Family"** The Yee family is glad they are safe. Their house was saved, too. They have put smoke detectors in their house. They joined the Neighborhood Watch program with Steve Meehan. Now they all watch out for their neighborhood.

Lesson 6

# Can't

**Learning Goals**
**Strategy:** Use your experience to help you understand what you read
**Reading:** Read a poem
**Skill:** Make inferences
**Writing:** Write a paragraph
**Word Work:** long *o* and long *u*

## Before You Read

"Can't" is a poem about an everyday hero. This person was afraid to try something. Before you read the poem, answer these questions.

1. Have you ever been afraid to try something because you might fail? If so, what was it?

_______________________________________________

_______________________________________________

2. Did you ever do something just to prove you could? If so, what?

_______________________________________________

_______________________________________________

3. Do you agree that doing something hard can make a person a hero? Why or why not?

_______________________________________________

_______________________________________________

## Key Words

- I once said I couldn't do it.
- I screamed it.
- I know you can't.
- I did prove them wrong.

## As You Read

In "Can't," the poet is afraid to try something. Then she changes her mind. As you read, think about what the poet might have been afraid to try.

# Can't

E. M. Marsh

I once said I couldn't do it
I screamed it
I yelled it
I told everyone

Then
One day
Someone said
"I know you can't"

Then I did it
To prove them wrong

## After You Read

**A.** Read the poem out loud.

**B.** Discuss these questions.

1. What happened in the first stanza? What might the poet have been afraid to try? How do you think the poet felt?
2. What happened in the second stanza that made her change her mind?
3. Why do you think the poet decided to do it?
4. Who do you think it is harder to convince about things—yourself or other people? Why?

## Think About It: Make Inferences

When you infer, you use clues to figure out something not said.

| Clue | Inference |
|---|---|
|  | 1. She has just come in from the rain. |
|  | 2. He has just built a dog house. |

## Practice

Answer the riddles. Use the words in the box.

| toast | sea | tree | today |
|---|---|---|---|

1. I am wet.
   I am blue.
   I have wave after wave.
   I am the ________________.

2. I am after yesterday.
   I am before tomorrow.
   I am now.
   I am ________________.

3. I am brown and dry.
   I get buttered.
   I used to be bread.
   I am ________________.

4. I am tall.
   I give shade in summer.
   I am bare in winter.
   I am a ________________.

## Write About It: Write a Paragraph

**A.** In "Can't," the poet did something that was hard for her to do. She proved to herself and to others that she could do it.

Think of something you have done that was hard for you. Finish these sentences. Or, if you prefer, write your own sentences.

I did a hard thing when ______________________________

I did not ______________________________

I wanted to ______________________________

I decided that ______________________________

It was ______________________________

I felt ______________________________

**B.** Copy your sentences into a paragraph.

______________________________

______________________________

______________________________

______________________________

______________________________

______________________________

______________________________

______________________________

## Word Work: Long *o* and Long *u*

**A. *o, oe, oa,* and *o–e* = Long *o*** Long *o* sounds like the *o* in *go*. Look at the words below. When you see words with these letters, give them the long *o* sound. Read the words.

| **o** | **oe** | **oa** | **o-e** |
|---|---|---|---|
| go | toe | goal | home |
| no | hoe | road | hope |
| hero | Joe | soap | broke |
| over | goes | toast | wrote |

**B. *u* and *u–e* = Long *u*** Long *u* sounds like the *u* in *use* or the *u* in *June*. Give the words below the sound of *u* as in *use*.

| **u** | **ue** | **u–e** |
|---|---|---|
| menu | argue | cute |
| music | rescue | mule |
| union | statue | refuse |
| united | value | perfume |

Give the words below the sound of *u* in *June*.

| **u** | **ue** | **u–e** |
|---|---|---|
| flu | due | tune |
| duty | blue | rule |
| ruby | glue | include |
| super | true | produce |

**C. Practice** Read these words. Cross out the word in each row that doesn't have a long vowel sound.

| | | | |
|---|---|---|---|
| **1.** rode | rope | road | rod |
| **2.** cute | cube | cut | clue |
| **3.** so | son | soap | spoke |
| **4.** hop | hope | hoe | hero |

**D. Word Families** Read the words in these word families. Write other words you know in each family on the lines.

| -oat | -one | -ore | -old | -use |
|---|---|---|---|---|
| boat | bone | more | old | fuse |
| float | tone | tore | bold | excuse |
| gloat | alone | store | cold | misuse |
| throat | phone | before | gold | refuse |
| ________ | ________ | ________ | ________ | ________ |

**E. More Practice** Pick the word pair that rhymes with the underlined words. Finish the rhymes. ✓Check off the word pairs as you use them.

| | | | |
|---|---|---|---|
| **alone** | **phone** | **✓boat** | **float** |
| **blue** | **true** | **hoe** | **toe** |

1. She put on her coat as the ___boat___ began to ___float___.

2. There is a tone on the __________. But he is not __________.

3. The rent is due. It's __________. I feel __________.

4. Joe hurt his __________ on my garden __________.

**F.** Work with a partner. Pick a word family. Write a rhyming sentence here.

________________________________________

________________________________________

________________________________________

# Review

## Reading Review

### Everyday Heroes

Heroes are people who do brave things. They do hard things that must be done. Rosa Parks was a hero. She took a stand in 1955, and an unfair law was changed. Cesar Chavez was a hero. He helped change farm workers' lives. Steve Meehan was a hero. He saved the Yee family.

Sometimes heroes do things no one thinks they can do. Sometimes heroes do things they didn't know they could do. This is what happened in the poem "Can't."

Think of the people you know. Maybe some of them are heroes, too.

Answer these questions. Write complete sentences.

1. What do we call people who do brave things?

_______________________________________________

2. In what year did Rosa Parks take a stand?

_______________________________________________

3. Who did Cesar Chavez help?

_______________________________________________

4. What kind of person do you think Steve Meehan is?

_______________________________________________

5. Why do you think the poet in "Can't" did what she did?

_______________________________________________

## Word Work Review

Pick the right word. Write it on the line.

1. Rosa Parks's story is ________________.
(trunk, true)

2. Rosa Parks ________________ the fare.
(pad, paid)

3. She took a ________________.
(sat, seat)

4. Steve saw the ________________.
(fir, fire)

5. He ________________ the Yees.
(saved, said)

6. Cesar Chavez helped ________________ workers.
(farm, frame)

7. He helped workers get ________________ pay.
(more, move)

## Write About It

**Topic:** Think of someone you feel is a hero. What has this person done to make him or her a hero?

**Prewrite** Discuss the topic questions. List some ideas.

**Write** Pick your best ideas. Write a paragraph about your hero.

**Revise** Look at your writing again. Change any words you want to change. Have someone read your writing. Can he or she understand it?

**Edit** Find and correct mistakes in your writing. See page 112.

**Final Draft** Make a final copy to keep and share.

Thrilling moments are important to us. We love moments that make our lives exciting.
Before you start Unit 3, think about thrilling times in your life.
What made those times special? What made them thrilling for you?

Lesson 7

# The Promotion

**Learning Goals**

**Strategy:** Use your experience to help you understand what you read
**Reading:** Read a story
**Skill:** Identify cause and effect
**Writing:** Write a story
**Word Work:** Digraphs (*ch, sh, th, ph, wh*)

## Before You Read

In "The Promotion," Rich Marsh has a special success at work. It is a thrilling moment for him. Before you read "The Promotion," answer these questions.

1. Think of a special success you have had. Was it at home? At work? At school? What was thrilling about this success?
2. ✓Check the sentences that are true for you. Write two more examples of your own.

   Things that have thrilled me:

   ____ winning a game or race

   ____ getting my first job

   ____ seeing my child for the first time

   ______________________________

   ______________________________

## Key Words

- Rich works at Alpha Company.
- He puts computer chips on thin boards.
- Things were not always good.
- Each Thursday the warehouse sent 10 boxes of chips.
- Ms. Chin thanked me.

## As You Read

In "The Promotion," Rich Marsh helps make things better at work. As you read, think about Rich. How does he feel about working for Alpha?

# The Promotion

My name is Rich Marsh. I work for the Alpha Company. I put computer chips on thin boards. I like my job now. But things were not always good.

My work team had problems. Each Thursday the warehouse sent us 10 boxes of chips. Some weeks we needed more chips. Then we had to sit and wait. We call this waiting "downtime."

Some weeks we needed fewer chips. But on Thursday we got 10 boxes anyway. Then we had to find some place to put them all.

Then I had an idea. I wanted to change the way boxes are sent. My boss, Ms. Chin, liked my idea. Now our team calls the warehouse when we are down to two boxes. We can call any day. We get 10 boxes the next day.

Now we get chips when we need them. We have no more downtime. We have no more boxes in the way. We save time. Ms. Chin is glad. She thanked me for helping my team to work better. Then she made me team leader! I was thrilled!

## After You Read

Discuss these questions.

**1.** What caused Rich to talk to Ms. Chin?

**2.** How does Rich feel about working for Alpha now? Why?

## Think About It: Identify Cause and Effect

In Lesson 2, you worked with cause and effect. A **cause** is what makes something happen. An **effect** is what happens.

## Practice

**A. Match** Write the letter of the correct effect next to the cause.

**Cause**

**Effect**

**1.** ____

**a.** 

**2.** ____

**b.** 

**3.** ____

**c.** 

**B. Match** Write the letter of the correct effect next to the cause.

**Cause**

____ **1.** Some weeks the team did not use all 10 boxes. But on Thursday 10 more boxes come.

____ **2.** Some weeks the team needed more than 10 boxes.

____ **3.** Rich had an idea.

**Effect**

**a.** The team had downtime.

**b.** Rich's team changed the way it worked.

**c.** The team ran out of space to store the boxes.

**C.** Copy the sentence that tells the effect of each cause.

- The team gets 10 boxes the next day.
- Rich got a promotion.
- The team sat and waited.

**1. Cause:** The team ran out of chips.

**Effect:** ____________________

**2. Cause:** The team calls the warehouse for more chips.

**Effect:** ____________________

**3. Cause:** Rich's idea worked well.

**Effect:** ____________________

## Write About It: Write a Story

Wise old sayings are called proverbs. They often tell about a cause and an effect.

**A. Match** Write the letter of the words that complete each proverb. Then talk about what each proverb means.

| | |
|---|---|
| b 1. Haste | a. killed the cat. |
| ____ 2. Waste not, | ✓ b. makes waste. |
| ____ 3. Curiosity | c. gets the worm. |
| ____ 4. United we stand, | d. want not. |
| ____ 5. The early bird | e. divided we fall. |

**B.** Here are more proverbs. Rewrite the proverbs in your own words. You may work with a partner. The first one is done for you.

**1. Proverb:** A stitch in time saves nine.

**Rewrite:** If you fix a problem before it gets big,

then you'll save yourself a lot of trouble.

**2. Proverb:** An apple a day keeps the doctor away.

**Rewrite:** If ____________________

then ____________________

**3. Proverb:** Absence makes the heart grow fonder.

**Rewrite:** If ____________________

then ____________________

**C.** Write the proverb endings or make up your own new ending.

**1.** When the cat's away ______________________________

**2.** April showers bring ______________________________

**3.** A penny saved is ______________________________

**D.** Find or make up another proverb. Then rewrite it with a partner.

**Proverb:** ______________________________

**Rewrite:** If ______________________________

then ______________________________

**E.** Choose one of the proverbs on these pages, or think of one of your own. Write a story that tells how the proverb came true for you. Write a title for your story.

______________________________

The proverb ______________________________

______________________________

______________________________

came true for me when ______________________________

______________________________

______________________________

I learned that ______________________________

______________________________

______________________________

## Word Work: Digraphs (*ch, sh, th, ph, wh*)

**A.** Two letters that spell one sound are called a **digraph.** Read these words. Do you hear one sound for each digraph?

| ch | sh | th | th | ph | wh |
|---|---|---|---|---|---|
| change | shower | thank | this | Alpha | when |
| cheer | shoe | thin | that | phone | what |
| children | fish | thing | father | nephew | whale |
| chin | ship | moth | than | Phil | why |
| reach | finish | bathtub | another | elephant | anywhere |

**B.** Look at each picture. Find the word in the lists above. Write it on the line.

______ ______ ______ ______

**C.** Use words from the lists above. Find words with *ch, sh, th, ph,* or *wh* for each group.

| People | Animals | Question Words | Things |
|---|---|---|---|
| nephew | fish | what | bathtub |
| ______ | ______ | ______ | ______ |
| ______ | ______ | ______ | ______ |

**D. Word Families** Use a digraph from the box to make a word for each word family. Then write one other word you know in each family.

| ch | ph | sh | th | wh |
|---|---|---|---|---|

| **-one** | **-eat** | **-in** | **-en** | **-ine** |
|---|---|---|---|---|
| phone | cheat | shin | then | whine |
| shone | ______ | ______ | ______ | ______ |
| bone | ______ | ______ | ______ | ______ |

**E.** Pick the right word for each sentence. Write it on the line.

1. Rich called a friend on the ________________.
   (phone, shone)
2. He said, "I met ________________ my boss today."
   (wish, with)
3. "Ms. ________________ liked my idea."
   (Thin, Chin)
4. "________________ made me team leader!"
   (The, She)

**Update on "The Promotion"** Rich's team works better now. And Rich has new ideas all the time. Last month Ms. Chin went to work at another Alpha plant. She wants Rich to work for her there. Rich likes these new and thrilling changes in his job.

Lesson 8

# The Thrill of the Race

**Learning Goals**
**Strategy:** Use what you know to understand what you read
**Reading:** Read a story
**Skill:** Sequence events
**Writing:** Make a list
**Word Work:** Three-letter initial blends (*scr, spl, spr, str, thr*)

## Before You Read

In "The Thrill of the Race," Phyllis Jones trains to run in the Boston Marathon. Before you read the story, discuss these questions.

1. What is a marathon? How is it different from other races?
2. Think of a marathon you have seen on TV or in real life. What do you remember about the runners? How did they look?
3. In a big marathon like the Boston Marathon, thousands of people run. Not every runner finishes the race. And only a few are winners. Why is it important for people to run when they know they probably won't win?

## Key Words

- Phyllis ran in the Boston Marathon.
- Phyllis stretched each day.
- She sprained her ankle.
- The race was held on Patriots' Day.
- Her friends screamed and cheered.
- Phyllis sprinted for the finish line.

## As You Read

In this story, Phyllis works hard to reach her goal. As you read, think about Phyllis's experience. How does it compare to what you already know about marathon runners?

# The Thrill of the Race

Phyllis Jones is 35 years old. She has always liked to run. This year she wanted a new thrill. She wanted to run in the Boston Marathon.

Phyllis trained hard for the 26-mile race. She stretched. She worked out. She ran each day. At one point, she sprained her ankle. But she didn't give up. At last she was in shape for the marathon.

The race was held on Patriots' Day in April. More than 5,000 runners waited for the starting gun. When it fired, the runners took off. The crowd cheered.

Phyllis made a strong start. Her friends saw her run by. They screamed and cheered. But the finish line was far away. She was hot. Her legs began to get sore. She wanted to stop. But she made herself go on. Finally Phyllis saw the finish line. She sprinted for it.

Phyllis finished the Boston Marathon! She ran all 26 miles, and she did it in just over three hours. What a thrill!

## After You Read

**A.** Retell Phyllis's story in your own words.

**B.** Discuss how Phyllis's experience compares with what you know about marathon runners.

## Think About It: Sequencing Events

In Lesson 1, you worked with sequence. **Sequence** is the order in which things happen.

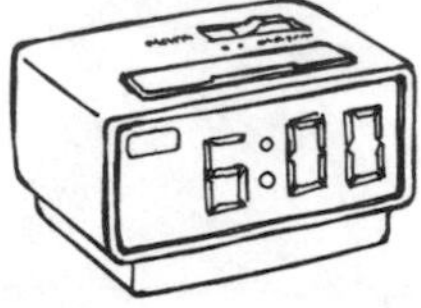


First it is time to get up.

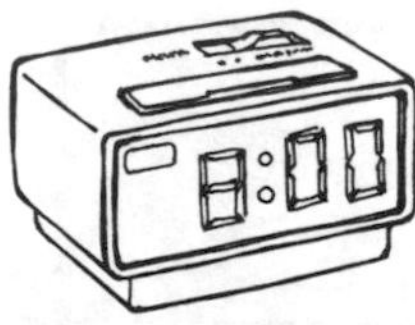


Second it is time to go to work.

Then it is time for lunch.

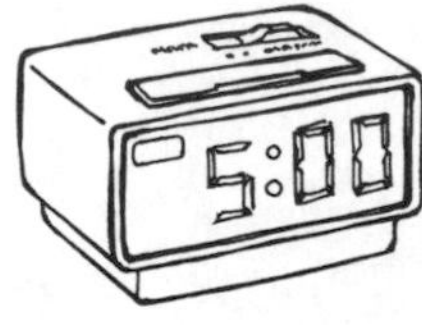


Last it is time to go home.

## Practice

**A.** Read the sentences. Number them in order. Then copy the correct sequence word next to each sentence.

| First | Second | Then | Last |
|---|---|---|---|

____ ________________ Phyllis finished in just over three hours.

____ ________________ Phyllis made a strong start in the race.

__1__ ________________ Phyllis wanted to run in the Boston Marathon.

____ ________________ Phyllis trained hard for the race.

**B.** Phyllis Jones works to stay fit. Look at the pictures of Phyllis's day.

First

Second

Then

Last

Read the sentences. Number them in order. Then copy the correct sequence word next to each sentence.

1 First Phyllis starts with a good breakfast.

___ __________ she gets the sleep she needs at night.

___ __________ she jogs or runs.

___ __________ she does warm-up stretches.

**C.** Copy the sentences in order. Write a title for your paragraph.

____________________

Each day Phyllis works hard to stay fit. First ____________________

## Write About It: Make a List

Phyllis's friends want to celebrate her thrilling run. They are planning a surprise party for her.

**A.** Unscramble the sentences to find out about the party. Write them on the lines.

### Plans for Phyllis's Party

| | |
|---|---|
| a to party surprise Phyllis for Come | Come to a surprise party for Phyllis! |
| ran the She marathon | ______________ |
| Joe's at party is The | ______________ |
| there Be 7 Friday at p.m. | ______________ |

**B.** Here are Joe's plans for the party. Copy them onto the right lines below.

- when the bell rings, everyone hides.
- everyone jumps out and yells "Surprise!"
- everyone gets here by 7 o'clock.
- Joe lets Phyllis in.

First everyone gets here by 7 o'clock.

Second, ______________

Then ______________

Last ______________

**C.** Work with a partner. Plan a party or celebration. List your plans. Here are some ideas to help you start.

### My Plans for a Party

| | | | |
|---|---|---|---|
| ____ | Clean the house. | ____ | ______________________ |
| ____ | Write a guest list. | ____ | ______________________ |
| ____ | Plan a menu. | ____ | ______________________ |
| ____ | Make phone calls. | ____ | ______________________ |

**D.** Number your list in the order in which you would do the tasks. Copy your list in the right order on the lines below.

**1.** ______________________

**2.** ______________________

**3.** ______________________

**4.** ______________________

**5.** ______________________

**6.** ______________________

**7.** ______________________

**8.** ______________________

## Word Work: Three-letter Initial Blends (*scr, spl, spr, str, thr*)

**A.** You can hear three sounds in most three-letter blends. Listen to these words.

| **scr** | **spl** | **spr** | **str** | **thr** |
|---|---|---|---|---|
| scrap | split | sprain | strain | three |
| scream | splash | spray | street | threw |
| screw | splice | spring | stretch | thrill |
| scrub | splendid | sprint | strong | thread |
| screen | splinter | sprout | strawberry | through |

**B.** Look at the pictures. Find the word above. Write the word on the line.

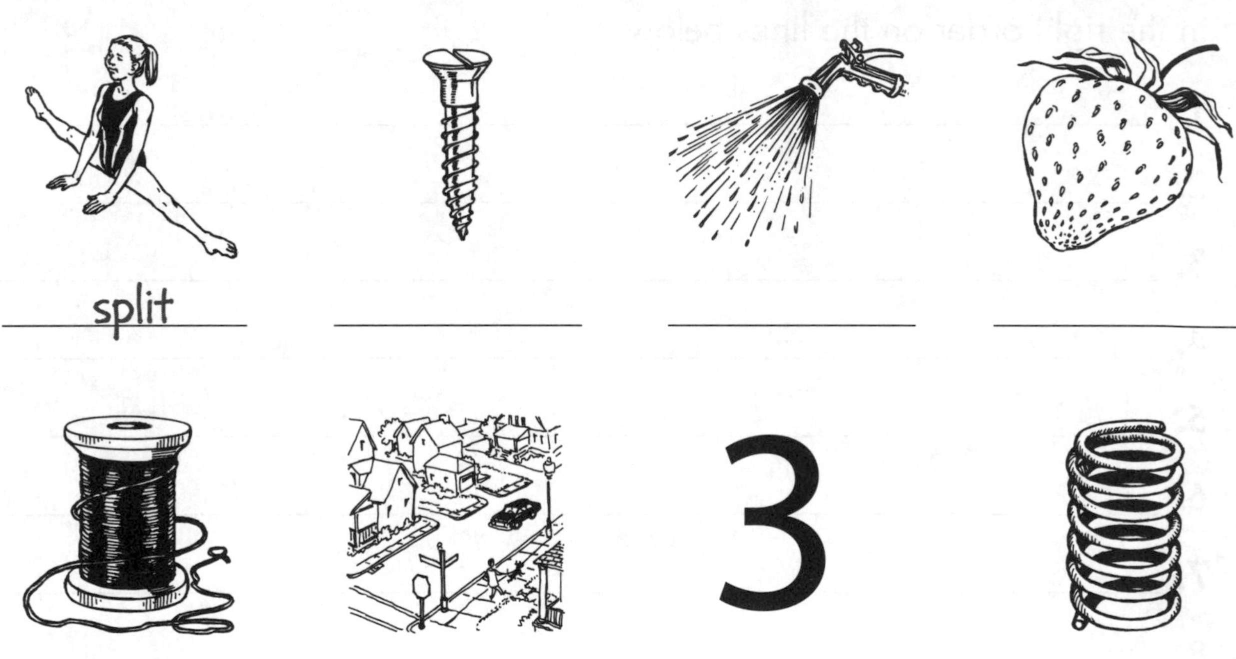


**C.** Cross out the word in each row that does not belong.

| | | | |
|---|---|---|---|
| **1.** thread | through | thank | threw |
| **2.** sting | strong | strain | street |
| **3.** spray | splash | sprain | sprout |
| **4.** scrub | scream | scrap | scold |

**D. Word Families** Use a three-letter blend from the box to make a new word in each word family. Then write another word you know in each family.

| scr | spl | spr | str | thr |
|---|---|---|---|---|

| -ain | -int | -ead | -eam | -ew |
|---|---|---|---|---|
| sprain | splint | spread | stream | screw |
| strain | ________ | ________ | ________ | ________ |
| ________ | ________ | ________ | ________ | ________ |

**E.** Pick the right word for each sentence. Write it on the line.

1. Phyllis wanted a new ________________. (thrill, spill)
2. She became a ________________ runner. (strong, throng)
3. She ________________ her ankle. (sprained, drained)
4. The race was held in the ________________. (string, spring)
5. Phyllis's friends ________________ and cheered. (screamed, dreamed)
6. Phyllis ________________ for the finish line. (printed, sprinted)

**Update on "The Thrill of the Race"** Phyllis still runs each day. She wants to keep fit. Some of her friends run with her now. They want to keep fit, too. What kinds of things do you do to keep fit?

Lesson 9

# Winner

**Learning Goals**
**Strategy:** Picture what you read
**Reading:** Read a poem
**Skill:** Make inferences
**Writing:** Write a poem
**Word Work:** Three-letter final blends (*nch, nce, nge, rse, dge*)

## Before You Read

In the poem "Winner," Gene Fehler describes a thrilling moment that a boy and his father shared. Before you read the poem, discuss these questions.

**1.** Think of a baseball game you have played or seen. What thrilling moments do you remember?

**2.** Do you remember a time when someone was very proud of something you did? How did it make you feel?

## Key Words

Here are some baseball terms that appear in the poem "Winner."

- **home plate:** where a batter stands to hit the ball
- **fast ball:** a pitch thrown at full speed
- **curve ball:** a pitch that curves unexpectedly before it reaches home plate
- **checked swing:** a swing of the bat that is started but not completed because the batter changes his or her mind
- **foul:** a baseball that is hit out of bounds or into foul territory
- **dying quail:** a softly hit ball that lands safely in front of the outfielder for a base hit
- **single:** a hit where the batter gets to first base safely
- **left-center:** just left of the middle of the outfield on a baseball field

## As You Read

In "Winner," the poet describes a thrilling moment from a man's childhood. As you read, try to see what the poet is saying. What pictures do you see in your mind?

# Winner

Gene Fehler

what I remember most
is my dad behind the rusted screen
back of home plate
"You can hit this guy!"
his voice not letting up
through four fast balls
(two misses swinging late,
two fouls on checked swings)
then the curve ball and the dying quail
into left-center,
the winning run sliding home,
my dad all smiles,
slapping backs in the bleachers
as if HIS single had won the game

## After You Read

**A.** Read the poem aloud.

**B.** Discuss these questions.

1. What happens in this poem? Retell it in your own words.
2. What pictures came to mind as you read this poem? What words does the poet use to help you see those pictures?
3. Picture the boy's dad during this game. Who is more thrilled by the boy's hit—the boy or his dad? Why do you think so?

## Think About It: Make Inferences

In Lesson 6, you worked with inferences. When you infer, you use clues to figure out something not said. What can you infer from the scenes below?

**What's the occasion?**

**1.** A new baby has been born.

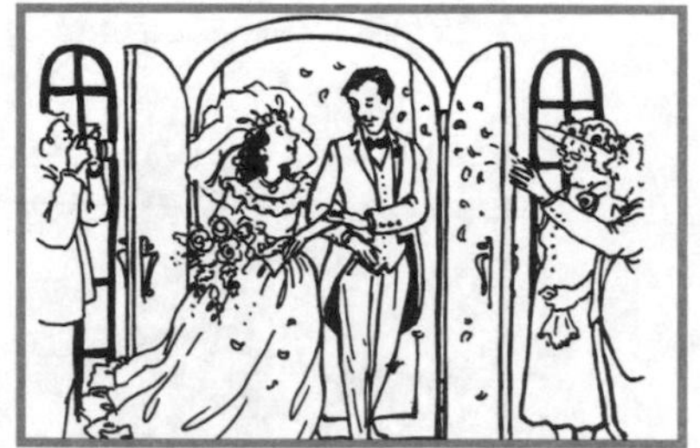

**2.** They just got married.

## Practice

Read the lines from the poem. ✓Check the inference that can be made.

**1.** what I remember most
is my dad behind the rusted screen

____ (1) The boy's dad being at the game was most important.

____ (2) The boy remembers the rusted screen best.

**2.** "You can hit this guy!"
his voice not letting up

____ (1) The boy's dad is calm.

____ (2) The boy's dad is excited.

**3.** then the curve ball and the dying quail . . .
the winning run sliding home

____ (1) The boy slid into home plate.

____ (2) The boy's hit won the game.

**4.** my dad . . . slapping backs in the bleachers
as if HIS single had won the game

____ (1) The boy's dad was very proud of him.

____ (2) The boy's dad won the game.

## Write About It: Write a Poem

**A.** "Winner" tells about a thrilling moment in a boy's life. Think of a thrilling moment you have had. Write about it here.

My thrilling moment was ____________________

I was ____________________

What I remember most is ____________________

____________________

I felt ____________________

I can still see ____________________

I can still hear ____________________

I can still taste ____________________

I can still feel ____________________

**B.** Pick your best ideas and write a poem. Here are some ways to start.

____________________

What I remember most ____________________

____________________

I was ____________________

I can still ____________________

____________________

I can still ____________________

____________________

It still makes me feel ____________________

____________________

## Word Work: Three-letter Final Blends (*nch, nce, nge, rse, dge*)

**A.** In Lesson 8, you read words that begin with three-letter blends. You can find three-letter blends at the ends of words, too. Read these words.

| -nch | -nce | -nge | -rse | -dge |
|---|---|---|---|---|
| inch | once | change | horse | edge |
| bench | fence | hinge | nurse | badge |
| branch | since | lunge | purse | fudge |
| lunch | prince | orange | course | bridge |

**B.** Read the two words under each picture. Pick the word that says what you see. Then write it on the line.

fence finch

______________

hedge hinge

______________

purse prince

______________

badge bridge

______________

**C.** Choose the right word to finish the sentences.

**1.** My dad and I had ________________ at the ball game.
(lunch, lunge)

**2.** We sat on a ________________ in the sun.
(badge, bench)

**3.** We had apples, ________________, bread, and cheese.
(oranges, changes)

**4.** Then we had some ________________.
(fence, fudge)

**D. Word Families** Read the word families and the words. Write other words you know in each family on the lines.

| **-ance** | **-ench** | **-inch** | **-inge** | **-edge** |
|---|---|---|---|---|
| dance | bench | cinch | hinge | hedge |
| chance | clench | clinch | cringe | wedge |
| France | wrench | pinch | twinge | pledge |
| ________ | ________ | ________ | ________ | ________ |

**E.** Unscramble each word to finish the sentences. The underlined word is a rhyming clue.

(Fernac) **1.** Lee learned to <u>dance</u> when he was in ________________.

(surpe) **2.** The <u>nurse</u> took her keys from the ________________.

(edweg) **3.** He cut the <u>hedge</u> into a ________________.

(chrewn) **4.** Fix the <u>bench</u> with this ________________.

(grenic) **5.** The sound of the <u>hinge</u> made me ________________.

**F.** Pick three words from the word families above. Scramble the letters and write the scrambled words here. Let a partner unscramble your words.

| **Your Scrambled Words** | **Partner's Real Words** |
|---|---|
| ________________ | ________________ |
| ________________ | ________________ |
| ________________ | ________________ |

# Review

## Reading Review

## Thrilling Moments

Thrilling moments are an important part of our lives. Thrilling moments can make us feel good. They can make us feel strong. They can help us prove just what we can do.

In Unit 3, you read about three people who had thrilling moments. Rich Marsh helped his team at the Alpha Company work better. This made him feel good. Phyllis Jones ran in the Boston Marathon. She was thrilled when she finished the race. A boy hit a winning single. He and his father were thrilled.

We also like to think of thrilling moments in our own lives. We like to share these moments with others, too. We like to have some excitement in our lives.

Choose the best answer to each question.

**1.** Which sentence best tells the main idea of "Thrilling Moments"?

____ (1) Rich Marsh helped his team work better.

____ (2) We like to share these moments with others.

____ (3) Thrilling moments are an important part of our lives.

**2.** Rich's idea helped his team save time. The team worked better. Which proverb best describes Rich's idea?

____ (1) Haste makes waste.

____ (2) A stitch in time saves nine.

____ (3) A friend in need is a friend indeed.

## Word Work Review

Unscramble each word to finish the sentences.

**1.** (thllnirig) Most people like ________________ moments.

**2.** (eedg) We like to sit on the ________________ of our seats.

**3.** (ceamrs) Some people ________________ when they are thrilled.

**4.** (resha) Most people like to ________________ their excitement.

**5.** (nepho) We may call our friends on the ________________.

**6.** (ocne) We may tell the story more than ________________.

**7.** (reeth) We may tell the story more than ________________ times.

**8.** (ngecha) Thrilling moments can ________________ our lives.

## Write About It

**Topic:** Think of a thrilling moment in your life. Why was it thrilling? Why was it important to you?

**Prewrite** Discuss the topic questions. List a few ideas.

**Write** Pick your best ideas. Write a paragraph about your thrilling moment.

**Revise** Look at your writing again. Change any words you want to change. Have someone read your writing. Can he or she understand it?

**Edit** Find and correct mistakes in your writing. See page 112.

**Final Draft** Make a final copy to keep and share.

What would we do without our friends? Friends share our lives. They help us when we are in trouble. They stay with us through good times and bad. Before you start Unit 4, think about the friends in your life. What do your friends add to your life? How do they make your life richer?

Lesson 10

# The Arch

**Learning Goals**

**Strategy:** Use what you know to help you understand what you read
**Reading:** Read a poem
**Skill:** Understand the main idea
**Writing:** Write a poem
**Word Work:** Special vowel combinations (*au, aw, oi, oy, oo,* and *ou*)

## Before You Read

In "The Arch," poet Shirley Kaufman uses the image of an arch to talk about friendship. Look at the picture of the arch on page 77. Then answer these questions.

1. Write a sentence that describes the arch.

______________________________

2. Where do you see arches? How are they used?

______________________________

3. Why do you think a poet might use the image of an arch when talking about friendship?

______________________________

## Key Words

- Half the world leans on the other half.
- An arch stands on two feet.
- You help me stand up straight and tall.
- We need the love and laughter of our friends.

## As You Read

As you read "The Arch," think about arches and about friendship. In what ways is an arch like two friends?

# The Arch

Shirley Kaufman

Half the world leans
on the other half
  to make it stand.

That's how an arch
stays up,
  two feet on land.

That's why I feel
so straight
  when you hold my hand.

## After You Read

**A.** Read the poem aloud.

**B.** Discuss these questions.

1. In what ways is an arch like two friends?
2. An arch is both strong and beautiful. Is an arch a good image for friendship? Why or why not?
3. How do you feel after reading this poem?

## Think About It: Understand the Main Idea

In Lesson 3, you worked with main idea. The main idea of a poem is its most important message.

Read "The Arch" again. Each stanza, or group of lines, tells about different types of support:

- leaning on each other
- helping each other stay up
- holding each other's hands

Even though the word *friend* does not appear in the poem, the stanzas lead us to infer that the main idea of the poem is:
**Friends support each other.**

## Practice

Read "Friends." Then answer the question.

**Friends**

We all need friends. We need their support. We need their advice. We need their love and laughter. We need friends because they help us get through life.

To have friends, we must also be a friend. It is as important to give support as it is to get it. It is as important to love as it is to be loved. We need to share with our friends. This helps us be all that we can be.

Which sentence best tells the main idea of "Friends"?

____ (1) We need their advice and their love.

____ (2) We need to give and get support.

____ (3) We all need to share with our friends.

## Write About It: Write a Poem

**A.** Here is another poem about friendship.

**Smiles**

A smile's like a bridge
  spanning the air.

People smile at each other
  to show they care.

That's why I feel happy
  when your smile is there.

**B.** Think of something that is like something else. Finish the sentence below.

A ________________ is like ________________.

**C.** Write your own poem. On a separate sheet of paper, write some ideas about how the two things you wrote are similar. Then pick your best ideas and write a poem on the lines below. Give your poem a title.

________________________________

________________________________________________________________

________________________________________________________________

________________________________________________________________

________________________________________________________________

________________________________________________________________

________________________________________________________________

## Word Work: Special Vowel Combinations (*au, aw, oi, oy, oo, ou*)

**A.** Some words have vowel sounds that aren't long or short. Words with the letter combinations below usually have special vowel sounds. Read the words. Listen to the vowel sounds.

| **au** as in **auto** | **aw** as in **saw** | **oi** as in **oil** | **oy** as in **boy** |
|---|---|---|---|
| fault | dawn | join | toy |
| taught | draw | noise | annoy |
| because | hawk | point | enjoy |
| daughter | awful | voice | employ |

**B.** Use word pairs from the box to complete the sentences. The underlined word has a rhyming clue in it.

| | | | |
|---|---|---|---|
| **auto** | **daughter** | **enjoyed** | **toy** |
| **dawn** | **hawk** | **spoiled** | **voices** |

**1.** I <u>saw</u> a ________________ in the sky at ________________.

**2.** Many <u>noises</u> and loud ________________ ________________ the play.

**3.** He <u>taught</u> his ________________ to drive the ________________.

**4.** The <u>boy</u> ________________ the new ________________ I gave him.

**C.** The letters *oo* and *ou* can make more than one sound. Read these words. Listen to the vowel sounds.

| **oo** as in **book** | **oo** as in **too** | **ou** as in **out** | **ou** as in **you** |
|---|---|---|---|
| cook | food | about | soup |
| foot | room | house | group |
| good | soon | proud | youth |
| took | school | sound | through |

**D.** Pick the word that fits in the sentence. Write it on the line.

1. We heard a very loud ______________.
   (soon, sound)

2. Will you finish reading that ______________ tonight?
   (book, boot)

3. Paula ______________ in every ______________.
   (locked, looked) (room, root)

4. They ate all the ______________ in the ______________.
   (food, foot) (hound, house)

5. The ______________ made hot ______________ for
   (cook, cool) (soap, soup)
   the ______________.
   (groan, group)

**E.** **Word Families** Read the words in these word families. Write another word you know for each family.

| **-aw** | **-oil** | **-ook** | **-ool** | **-ound** |
|---|---|---|---|---|
| jaw | boil | book | cool | bound |
| paw | coil | hook | pool | found |
| saw | broil | look | tool | sound |
| claw | spoil | brook | stool | ground |
| ________ | ________ | ________ | ________ | ________ |

**F.** Work with a partner. Pick a word family. Use at least two of the words to write a rhyming sentence.

______________________________________________

______________________________________________

Lesson 11

# A Special Friend

**Learning Goals**
**Strategy:** Use your experience to help you understand what you read
**Reading:** Read three poems
**Skill:** Find details
**Writing:** Complete a diagram
**Word Work:** R-controlled vowels (*are, err, ire, ore, ure*)

## Before You Read

This lesson has three poems about friends. Think of a friend who is important to you. Answer these questions.

**1.** ✓Check your choices. Add your own.

A friend is someone I can

____ laugh with　　____ talk to

____ depend on　　____ trust

__________________

__________________

**2.** Complete this sentence.

I know someone is a good friend when ____________________________

________________________________________________________

## Key Words

- My best friend is a special person.
- My friend shows me love and appreciation.
- We share trust and honesty.
- My friend listens and pays attention to what I say.
- My friend gives me a generous smile.

## As You Read

"A Special Friend" was written by a student at the Adult Literacy Resource Institute in Boston. As you read, think about how the poet describes a special friend. Do you agree?

# A Special Friend

Toni

a special friend's
a special blessing

a special friend's,
someone to talk to,

someone to laugh with,
someone to hold on to

a special friend's
someone who shows you love, appreciation
and honesty.

## After You Read

**A.** Read the poem aloud.

**B.** Discuss these questions.

1. How does the poet describe a special friend?
2. Which quality listed in the poem do you feel is most important in a friend? Why do you feel this way?
3. What, if anything, would you add to the description?
4. As you read, did you picture someone you know? If you did, who was it?

## Think About It: Find Details

In Lesson 5, you practiced finding details. Details are the pieces of information you find in readings. Details often support the main idea of the reading.

Read "A Special Friend" once more. The main idea of the poem is this:
**A special friend is a special blessing.**

**A.** The poem has many details to support this main message. ✓Check each detail that you find in the poem.

A special friend is a special blessing because that person is someone

**1.** ____ to talk to

**2.** ____ you can laugh with

**3.** ____ you can hold on to

**4.** ____ you can fight with

**5.** ____ who shows you love

**6.** ____ who appreciates you

**7.** ____ who is honest

**8.** ____ who is in your family

Did you check details 1, 2, 3, 5, 6, and 7? If so, you found the details in the poem.

**B.** You can organize details in a diagram like the one below to show how they relate to the main idea.

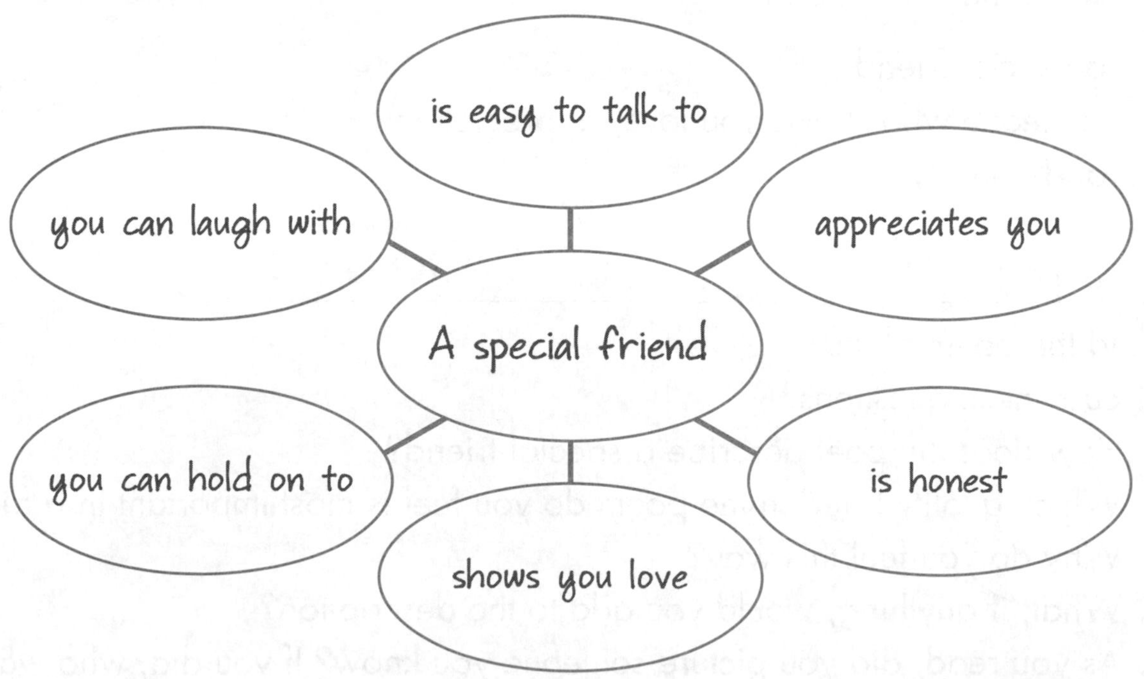

## Practice

**A.** Read this poem. Think about the main idea. Look for details that support the main idea.

**JC and Me**

Jonathan Cook comes from New York City.
I come from down on a farm.
Jonathan Cook has curly black hair
while mine is as straight as your arm.
Jonathan Cook loves to sing and to dance.
I like to watch and to see.
Jonathan lives with five sons and three dogs.
At home there's my girlfriend and me.

But we're as alike as two people can be,
my good friend JC and me.
We know what we want and we know where we'll go.
We talk and we trust and we laugh and we know
that our friendship will always be.

**B.** Read the poem aloud.

**C.** Answer these questions.

**1.** What is the main idea of "JC and Me"?

____ (1) They may have differences, but the two are best friends.

____ (2) The two friends are as alike as people can be.

**2.** List two details that show how the friends are different.

______________________________ ______________________________

**3.** List two details that show how the friends are alike.

______________________________ ______________________________

## Write About It: Complete a Diagram

**A.** You have read two poems about friendship. Here is another poem. It was written by an adult literacy student in Superior, Wisconsin. As you read, notice the details. Guess who the poet's best friend is.

### My Best Friend

Dan Mosack

Is she worth it?
Every day, same old thing.
Buy food, comb her hair.
Always having to be there
  for her.
Is she worth it?
Messy, all the time messy,
Always having to clean her
  messes.
Is she worth it?
Yeah, she's always there
  for me.
When I need to talk to someone,
She listens, paying close attention
  to what I say.
Is she worth it?
Come to think of it she's always
  been there for me.
Never been alone.
She goes almost everywhere I go.
Is she worth it?
A daily hug, a daily walk, a
  generous smile.
Warm and cuddly, honest and true.
Is she worth it?
You bet she's worth it.
Flopsy my English Springer and me
  are friends forever.

**B.** Answer these questions.

1. Who is the poet's best friend? ______________________

2. At what point in the poem did you guess that Dan's best friend is a dog? Put a star (*) by that place in the poem.

3. Find details in the poem that hint that Flopsy is a dog. Copy some of the details here.

______________________ ______________________

______________________ ______________________

**C.** In "My Best Friend," the poet gives details that show why Flopsy is such a good friend. We can picture these details in a diagram like the one below. At the center of the diagram is Flopsy. Around Flopsy are the details.

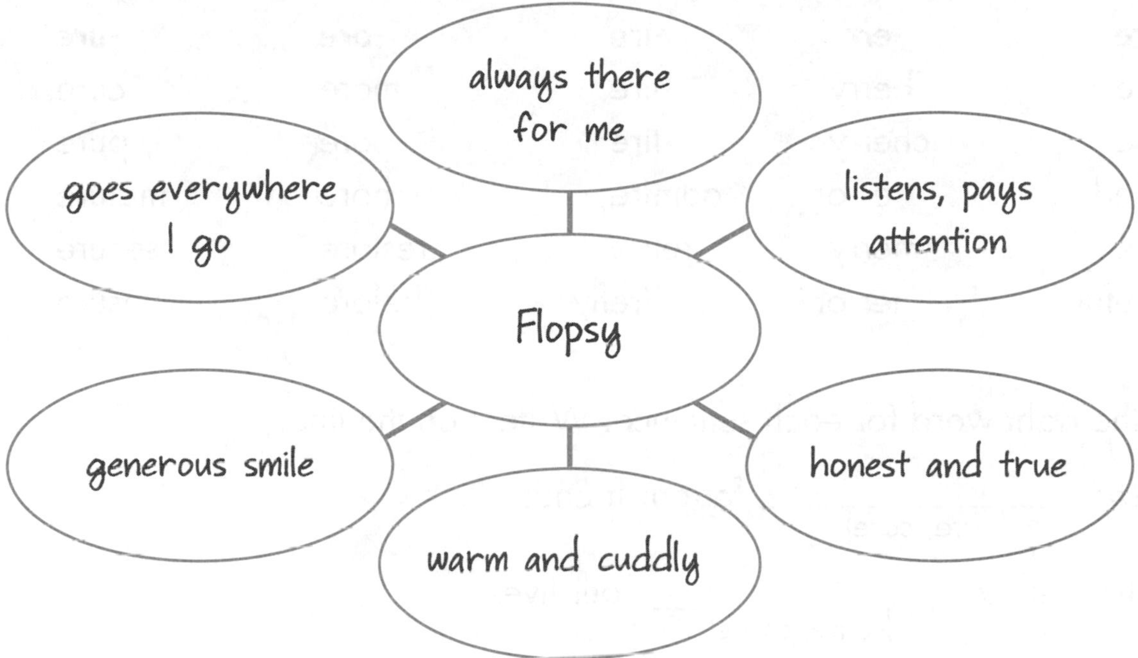


**D.** Think of your best friend, or a friend you feel is special. Think about why this person is special. What makes this person a good friend?

Write your friend's name in the center of the diagram. Fill in the rest of the diagram with details that show why this person is such a good friend.

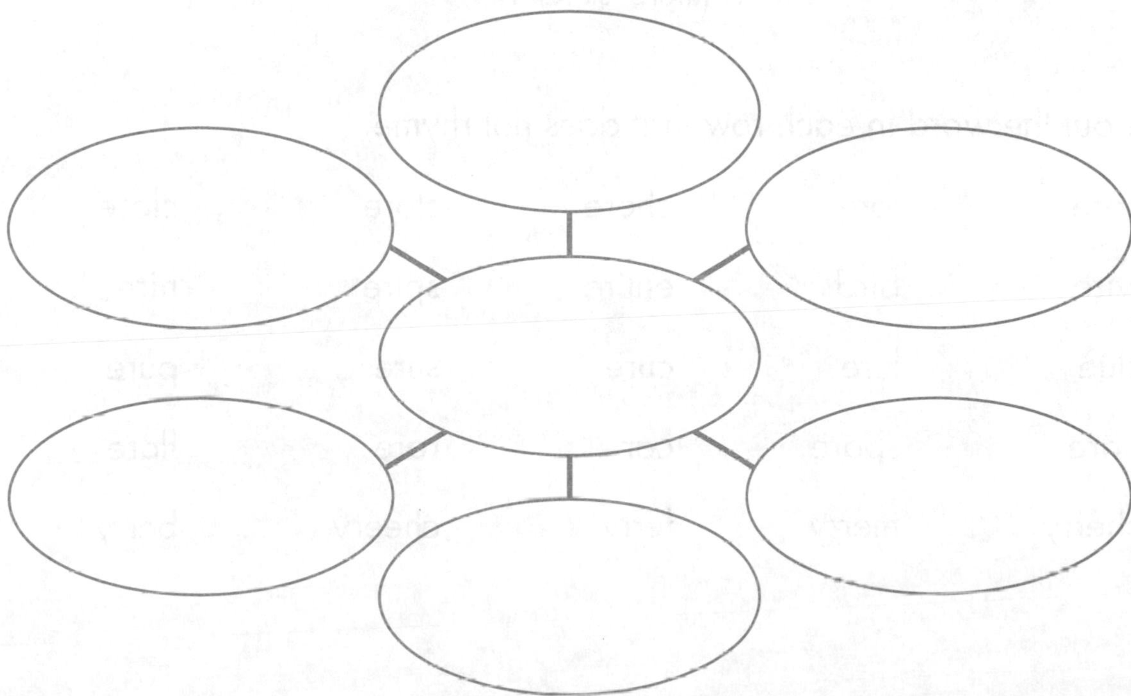

## Word Work: R-controlled Vowels (*are, err, ire, ore, ure*)

**A.** When a vowel is followed by *r*, the sound of the vowel changes slightly. Read the words below. Listen to the vowel sounds.

| -are | -err | -ire | -ore | -ure |
|---|---|---|---|---|
| dare | berry | hire | more | cure |
| fare | cherry | tire | sore | pure |
| scared | error | admire | shore | mature |
| share | merry | retire | restore | secure |
| careful | terror | firefly | before | unsure |

**B.** Pick the right word for each sentence. Write it on the line.

**1.** We ________________ for our friends.
(dare, care)

**2.** Our friends ________________ our lives.
(scare, share)

**3.** We feel ________________ our friends will help us.
(cure, sure)

**4.** Friends ________________ each other.
(retire, admire)

**5.** Friends make our lives ________________ complete.
(more, store)

**C.** Cross out the word in each row that does not rhyme.

| | | | | | |
|---|---|---|---|---|---|
| **1.** | core | tore | chore | store | close |
| **2.** | wire | bird | entire | spire | hire |
| **3.** | clue | lure | cure | sure | pure |
| **4.** | bare | spare | car | rare | flare |
| **5.** | cherry | merry | ferry | cheery | berry |

**D. Crossword Puzzle** Use the clues to help you fill in the words from the Word List.

**ACROSS**

1. Toni's poem is about a __________ friend.
3. Things we have to do
6. Looks up to
9. What you do in a marathon
10. Give half to
11. Truthful
13. Fix like new
15. Opposite of left
18. Safe
19. They follow causes.

**DOWN**

1. Afraid
2. Hear
3. Auto
4. Have
5. Edge of the water
7. Like an adult; grown up
8. Opposite of poor
10. Place to buy things
12. All of us
13. Stop working
14. Great fear
16. Has faith in
17. Opposite of on

**WORD LIST**

ADMIRES
CAR
CHORES
EFFECTS
EVERYONE
HONEST
LISTEN
MATURE
OFF
OWN
RESTORE
RETIRE
RICH
RIGHT
RUN
SCARED
SECURE
SHARE
SHORE
SPECIAL
STORE
TERROR
TRUSTS

Lesson 12

# Sofia's Journal

**Learning Goals**
**Strategy:** Picture what you read
**Reading:** Read a journal entry
**Skill:** Make predictions
**Writing:** Make a journal entry
**Word Work:** More R-controlled Vowels (*ar, er, ear, our*)

## Before You Read

In this lesson, you will read some pages from Sofia's personal journal. Sofia comes from Turkey. She writes about her life in the journal. She writes about her thoughts, feelings, and what she is doing. Before you read her journal entries, answer these questions.

1. Look at the picture on page 91. What do you think Sofia will write about today? Make a prediction. Write it here.

   ______________________________

2. Talk about keeping a journal. What kinds of things would you write? How would keeping a journal help you improve your reading and writing skills?

3. Many people lose touch with friends as years go by. What are some reasons people lose touch? List some reasons here.

   ______________________________

   ______________________________

   ______________________________

## Key Words

- My friend <u>arrived</u> from <u>Turkey</u>.
- We <u>laughed</u> and <u>cried</u> at the same time.
- <u>Kemal</u> is a <u>charming</u> <u>young</u> boy.
- We played <u>Turkish music</u>.
- What a joy to be <u>together</u> <u>again</u>.

## As You Read

In her journal, Sofia writes about a reunion with her old friend, Meral. What pictures come to mind as you read?

# Sofia's Journal

June 5

Dear Journal,

What a week I've had! On Monday, my old friend, Meral, arrived from Turkey! I had not seen her for many years. But I knew her right away. Her black hair and eyes still shine like the night. And who can forget her big smile?

She knew me right away, too. When she saw me, she yelled, "Sofia, you have not changed!" We ran into each other's arms. We laughed and cried at the same time. Everyone stared at us.

When I saw Meral last, she was a girl. Now she is a woman. Her son Kemal is with her. He is 10. He is a charming young boy. And so smart!

Last night I had a party for Meral and Kemal. I cooked Turkish food. We played Turkish music. We danced folk dances all night. We all ate and sang and danced. What a joy to be together again!

## After You Read

**A.** Retell Sofia's story in your own words.

**B.** Discuss these questions.

1. What pictures came to mind as you read this journal entry?
2. How would you feel if you did not see a close friend for many years? How would you feel when you finally saw that person again?

## Think About It: Make Predictions

In Lesson 4, you practiced predicting. When you predict, you try to figure out what will be in a reading. You can use the title and the pictures to help you predict.

You made a prediction about Sofia on page 90. Copy it here.

______________________________________________

How did your prediction match the story? How did it not match?

______________________________________________

______________________________________________

## Practice

**A.** Read each title and look at each picture. ✓Check the prediction that can be made.

**1. Title:** You Never Know Until You Try

**Prediction:** (1) ____ She will get fired.

(2) ____ She will apply for the job.

(3) ____ She will not try to get a job.

**2. Title:** Beating Fear

**Prediction:** (1) ____ He will be afraid to jump.

(2) ____ He will break his leg.

(3) ____ He will jump from the plane.

**B.** Read each title and look at each picture. Predict what may happen. Write your prediction.

**1. Title:** Gold Medal Day

**Prediction:** ______________________________

______________________________

**2. Title:** A New Heart, a New Life

**Prediction:** ______________________________

______________________________

**C.** Look at the picture. Write your own title. Let a partner predict what may happen.

**Title:** ____________________

**Prediction:** ______________________________

______________________________

## Write About It: Make a Journal Entry

**A.** Sofia began writing in a journal when she was young. Here is a page she wrote a long time ago. How is this entry different from the entry on page 91? How is it similar?

**My Journal**

May 12

Hello Journal,

My teacher gave me this journal today. She said it will make me feel better. It will help my writing, too. I have been very sad. I miss my friend, Meral, very much. Mother and Father wanted to move to the U.S. They want to be with the rest of our family. Meral had to stay with her family in Turkey.

Mother and Father like living here. I like it, too. I like my school. I like being near my Grandmother and Grandfather. But it would be better if Meral were here. We are so far away. I think I will not see her for a long time. I will write her a letter today.

Thank you, Journal, for being here today.

**1.** Sofia made a prediction in this journal entry. Copy it here.

______________________________________________

Was her prediction correct? How can you tell?

**2.** Underline the part of this entry that you like best. Tell why you like it. Then rewrite that part in your own words.

______________________________________________

______________________________________________

**B.** Many things can change a friendship. A birth, a death, or a marriage can change a friendship. Moving to a new place can change a friendship, too.

Think about a change in a friendship you have had. Think about why it changed. Think about how you felt. Did you like the change? Did it make you happy or sad? Write a journal entry about that time.

____________________
(date)

Dear Journal,

## Word Work: More R-controlled Vowels (*ar, er, ear, our*)

**A.** ***ar:*** The letters *ar* can make different sounds in different words. Listen to the words. Then read the sentences.

**arm** The mark on his arm was a scar.

**warm** I warmed a quart of milk.

**marry** She will marry Gary in January.

Write each word under the *ar* sound you hear. Then write a word of your own.

| charm | quart | parent | award | part | vary |
|---|---|---|---|---|---|

| arm | warm | marry |
|---|---|---|
| ______ | ______ | ______ |
| ______ | ______ | ______ |
| ______ | ______ | ______ |

**B.** ***er:*** The letters *er* can make different sounds in different words. Listen to the words. Then read the sentences.

**very** The merit awards ceremony was very nice.

**hero** The hero in the series was superior.

**her** Her clerk was nervous.

Read the words in each list. On your own paper, write three sentences using as many words from the lists as you can.

| very | hero | her |
|---|---|---|
| peril | here | term |
| stereo | zero | nerve |
| American | period | Germany |

**C.** ***ear:*** The letters *ear* can make different sounds in different words. Listen to the words. Then read the sentences.

**hear** I hear you, dear, loud and clear.

**wear** The bear will tear what I wear.

**heard** Pearl heard the news early.

Write each word under the *ear* sound you hear. Then write a word of your own.

| appear | earth | swear | fear | learn | pear |
|---|---|---|---|---|---|

| hear | wear | heard |
|---|---|---|
| __________ | __________ | __________ |
| __________ | __________ | __________ |
| __________ | __________ | __________ |

**D.** ***our:*** The letters *our* can make different sounds in different words, too. Listen to the words. Then read the sentences.

**our** Our milk will sour in an hour.

**four** Your friend will pour four more.

**journey** The jungle journey took courage.

Read the words in each list. On your own paper, write three sentences using as many words from the lists as you can.

| our | four | journey |
|---|---|---|
| flour | your | adjourn |
| scour | court | journal |
| hourly | mourn | courtesy |

# Review

## Reading Review

## Friends

Friends are an important part of our lives. In Unit 4, you read some writers' ideas about friendship. One poet told how a friend's support makes her "feel so straight." Another wrote of what it takes to be a best friend. A third poet told why his dog is his best friend. Sofia wrote in her journal about seeing an old friend.

Think of the good friends in your life. Your friends may be in your family. They may be neighbors or people you work with. They may be near or far away. No matter where they are, one thing is true. Your friends play an important part in your life.

Answer these questions.

**1.** Which sentence best tells the main idea of "Friends"?

____ (1) Your friends may be in your family.

____ (2) Friends are an important part of our lives.

____ (3) Think of the good friends in your life.

**2.** ✓Check two details that are in the reading.
Friends may be

____ (1) in your family

____ (2) neighbors

____ (3) old or young

## Word Work Review

Finish the sentences. Use a word in the box that rhymes with the underlined word.

| |
|---|
| about |
| bear |
| care |
| far |
| four |
| near |
| store |
| very |

1. We share because we _______________.
2. A good car can take you _______________.
3. She got more food at the _______________.
4. The berry pie is _______________ good.
5. I fear that the time is _______________.
6. I found out _______________ the surprise.
7. I heard it from your _______________ friends.
8. I gave my pear to the big black _______________.

## Write About It

**Topic:** Think of a special time you had with a friend. What happened? What made this time special?

**Prewrite** Discuss the topic questions. List some ideas.

**Write** Pick your best ideas. Write a paragraph about your special time.

**Revise** Look at your writing again. Change any words you want to change. Have someone read your writing. Can he or she understand it?

**Edit** Find and correct mistakes in your writing. See page 112.

**Final Draft** Make a final copy to keep and share.

# Writing Skills Mini-Lesson:
## Sentences and Capitalization

When you write sentences, be sure they are complete. Be sure they are capitalized correctly. Follow these rules:

1. **A sentence states a complete thought. It begins with a capital letter and ends with a period.**
   **I** have a dream.
2. **A question begins with a capital letter and ends with a question mark.**
   **W**hat is your dream?
3. **Always capitalize the word *I*. Capitalize people's names.**
   **D**on **G**rant and **I** each have a dream.
   **W**hat is our dream?
   **D**on wants a new job, and so do **I**.

### Practice

Rewrite each sentence. Capitalize the correct words. Write a period (.) or a question mark (?) at the end of each sentence.

1. don grant wants a better job

   ______________________________

2. he wants to make more money, and so do i

   ______________________________

3. how will don and i get new jobs

   ______________________________

4. he and i will have to work hard to get them

   ______________________________

# Writing Skills Mini-Lesson:

## Contractions

A **contraction** is formed when two words are combined into one. At least one letter is dropped. An **apostrophe** takes the place of the missing letter or letters.

can not ➡ can't     is not ➡ isn't

Here are some other common contractions.

| | | |
|---|---|---|
| are not | ➡ | aren't |
| was not | ➡ | wasn't |
| were not | ➡ | weren't |
| do not | ➡ | don't |
| does not | ➡ | doesn't |
| did not | ➡ | didn't |

| | | |
|---|---|---|
| has not | ➡ | hasn't |
| have not | ➡ | haven't |
| had not | ➡ | hadn't |
| will not | ➡ | won't |
| could not | ➡ | couldn't |
| would not | ➡ | wouldn't |

### Practice

**A.** Write the contraction.

**1.** did not ___didn't___

**2.** do not __________

**3.** is not __________

**4.** has not __________

**5.** could not __________

**6.** would not __________

**B.** Rewrite each sentence. Put the apostrophe (') in each contraction.

**1.** She thinks she cant do it.

______________________________

**2.** Isnt it time for her to try?

______________________________

**3.** She wont give up now.

______________________________

# Writing Skills Mini-Lesson:

## Plurals

Plural means more than one. Most plurals are formed by adding *-s* or *-es* to a word. To make a word plural, follow these rules.

1. **Add *-s* to most words.**

   job + s = jobs     game + s = games     day + s = days

2. **Add *-es* to words ending in *s, x, z, ch,* and *sh*.**

   boss + es = bosses     box + es = boxes     wish + es = wishes

3. **If a word ends in a consonant + *y*, change the *y* to *i* and add *-es*.**

   city + es = cities     company + es = companies

### Practice

**A.** Write the plurals.

**1.** car + s ____________________

**2.** class + es ____________________

**3.** party + es ____________________

**4.** bench + es ____________________

**B.** Make each word plural. Write the plural word on the line.

**1.** (idea) Rich Marsh has many good ____________________.

**2.** (worker) He is one of the best ____________________ at Alpha.

**3.** (boss) Someday he may be one of the ____________________.

**4.** (stretch) Phyllis did many warm-up ____________________.

**5.** (story) There are many ____________________ about baseball.

**6.** (family) Friends and ____________________ come to see them play.

# Writing Skills Mini-Lesson:

## Adding *-ed* and *-ing*

When adding *-ed* or *-ing* to a word, follow these rules.

1. **Add *-ed* or *-ing* to most words without changing anything.**

   warn + ed = warned     enjoy + ed = enjoyed
   warn + ing = warning     enjoy + ing = enjoying

2. **If a word ends in silent *e*, drop the *e* before adding *-ed* or *-ing*.**

   hope + ed = hoped     change + ed = changed
   hope + ing = hoping     change + ing = changing

3. **If a word ends with a short vowel followed by a consonant, double the consonant before adding *-ed* or *-ing*. Do not double *w* or *x*.**

   hop + ed = hopped     plan + ed = planned
   hop + ing = hopping     plan + ing = planning

### Practice

**A.** Add *-ed* or *-ing* to each word. Write the word on the line.

**1.** retire + ed = ____________     **4.** run + ing = ____________

**2.** want + ed = ____________     **5.** make + ing = ____________

**3.** hop + ed = ____________     **6.** buy + ing = ____________

**B.** Add *-ed* or *-ing* to finish the sentences.

**1.** (stop + ed) My friend ____________ by to see me.

**2.** (smile + ing) My friend is ____________ at me.

**3.** (help + ing) My friend is always ____________ me.

**4.** (hug + ed) My friend ____________ me today.

# Answer Key

## Unit 1 Hopes and Dreams

### Lesson 1

**After You Read (p. 5)**

1. Ken wants to read to his son.
   Jan wants to work in a shop.
   Brad wants to go to college and get a better job.
2. They are going to school to learn to read better.

**Think About It: Sequence Events (p. 6)**
**Practice**

B. 1, 3, 2
   Then, Last, First

C. 2, 1, 3
   2. Then Ken learns to read and write better.
   3. Last Ken reads stories to Russ.

D. 2, 3, 1
   Then Jan learns to read better.
   Last Jan gets a job in a shop.

**Word Work: Short Vowels (p. 10)**

B. pet, pin, mop, cut
   hat, bed, pen, nut

C. Word order may vary. Words should include:

| | | |
|---|---|---|
| ham | bat | lack |
| hem | bet | lick |
| him | bit | lock |
| hum | but | luck |

### Lesson 2

**After You Read (p. 13)**

Wording may vary.

1. Sal comes from Mexico.
2. Sal came to Texas because he wanted a better life.
3. Each day Sal worked hard and went to class.
4. He learned to speak English.
5. Sal's new dream is to visit his family in Mexico.

**Think About It: Identify Cause and Effect (p. 14)**
**Practice**

A. 1. c
   2. a
   3. b

B. 2. (1) He misses his family.
   3. (1) He wanted a better job.

C. Sentences may be similar to these:
   **Effect:** Sal has finished school.
   **Cause:** Sal went to class and studied hard.

**Word Work: Initial Consonant Blends (p. 18)**

B. clock, stop, grass, broom
   star, plant, brush, plate

D. 2. class
   3. state
   4. plans
   5. glad

### Lesson 3

**After You Read (p. 21)**

Possible answers:

2. Do not give up your dreams.
3. A bird with broken wings cannot fly. It can be caught. Similarly, a person without dreams has no hope. He or she can get trapped in a bad situation.
4. Nothing grows in a barren field. Similarly, a person without dreams does not grow, nor does he or she help others to grow.

**Think About It: Understand the Main Idea (p. 22)**
**Practice**

1. Life is a barren field frozen with snow.
2. Possible answers: crippled, torn, fractured, empty, bare, deserted
3. Possible answers: If we hold on to our dreams, life is a bird that can fly high in the sky; Life is a field full of flowers and plants.

**Word Work: Final Consonant Blends (p. 24)**

B. lamp, child, best, gift
   pump, field, cent, stamp

D. Crossword Puzzle

| | | | | | | | | | |
|---|---|---|---|---|---|---|---|---|---|
| | | | | | | O | W | N | |
| | | | | H | | | I | | |
| | | B | R | O | K | E | N | | |
| | | A | | L | | | G | | S |
| | | R | | D | | L | E | F | T |
| | | R | | | | | D | | A |
| F | I | E | L | D | | | | | M |
| A | | N | | | C | L | A | M | P |
| S | | | | | H | | | | |
| T | E | N | T | | E | | | | |
| | | O | | | S | W | I | F | T |
| | | W | E | N | T | | | | |

## Unit 1 Review (p. 26)

**Reading Review**

1. (1) In this unit, we learned about some hopes and dreams.
2. (1) They want to read better.
3. (2) He wanted a better life.

**Word Work Review**

1. class
2. has
3. shop
4. job
5. plan
6. hold
7. best

## Unit 2 Everyday Heroes

### Lesson 4

**After You Read (p. 29)**

**A.** Wording may vary.

1. First Rosa Parks paid her fare and sat down.
2. A white man wanted her seat.
3. Ms. Parks did not give her seat to the white man.
4. She was arrested.

**Think About It: Make Predictions (p. 30)**
**Practice**

A. 1. (2) The man will learn to cook dinner.
   2. (1) They will take a trip to Mexico.

**B. and C.** Answers will vary.

**Word Work: Long *a* and Long *i* (p. 33)**

B. rain, cape, sail, plane

C. 1. tape, made, Jane
   2. rain, pain, paid, main

D. 1. *e* 2. long

F. 1. ride 5. fight
   2. bite 6. fine
   3. sight 7. spine
   4. dime 8. ripe

G. 1. *e* 2. long

H. 3.

J. 1. ride 4. life
   2. white 5. admire
   3. right

### Lesson 5

**After You Read (p. 37)**

B. 2. through the window
   3. because he saved their lives

**Think About It: Find Details (p. 38)**

A. 2. True
   3. False
   4. True
   5. True

B. 1. 5 Beach Street
   2. Ms. Yee and her baby
   3. first-floor window
   4. fire fighters
   5. OK, safe, *or* fine
   6. brave

**Practice**

B. 1. Pete Greeley
   2. Friday
   3. today or after 25 years
   4. prizes and medals
   5. brave

**Write About It: Write About a Person You Interview (p. 40)**

A. 2. a
   3. d
   4. e
   5. c

B. 1. What
   2. Where *or* When
   3. Where
   4. What
   5. What

**Word Work: Long *e* and Long *y* (p. 42)**

C. 1. and 3.

**Practice**

E. 1. Why
   2. bravery
   3. easy

F. 2. pet
   3. bet
   4. fed
   5. head
   6. flat

### Lesson 6

**After You Read (p. 45)**

Possible answers:

B. 1. The poet felt afraid or upset.
   2. Someone agreed that the poet could not do something. This made the poet think twice.
   3. She says she wanted to convince "them," but she also wanted to convince herself.

**Think About It: Make Inferences (p. 46)**
**Practice**

1. sea
2. today
3. toast
4. tree

### Word Work: Long *o* and Long *u* (p. 48)

C. 1. rod
   2. cut
   3. son
   4. hop

E. 2. phone, alone
   3. true, blue
   4. toe, hoe

## Unit 2 Review (p. 50)

### Reading Review

Possible answers:

1. We call them heroes.
2. Rosa Parks took a stand in 1955.
3. He helped farm workers.
4. He is brave.
5. Answers will vary.

### Word Work Review

1. true
2. paid
3. seat
4. fire
5. saved
6. farm
7. more

# Unit 3 Thrilling Moments

## Lesson 7

### After You Read (p. 53)

1. His team had problems with the chips they needed. Rich had on idea to solve the problem.
2. He likes working for Alpha now. The problems with the computer chips are solved. His team works better now. Rich got a promotion.

### Think About It: Identify Cause and Effect (p. 54)

### Practice

A. 1. b
   2. c
   3. a

B. 1. c. The team ran out of space to store the boxes.
   2. a. The team had downtime.
   3. b. Rich's team changed the way it worked.

C. 1. The team sat and waited.
   2. The team gets 10 boxes the next day.
   3. Rich got a promotion.

### Write About It: Write a Story (p. 56)

A. 2. d; Waste not, want not.
   3. a; Curiosity killed the cat.
   4. e; United we stand, divided we fall.
   5. c; The early bird gets the worm.

B. Answers will vary.

C. Possible answers:
   1. the mice will play.
   2. May flowers.
   3. a penny earned.

### Word Work: Digraphs (p. 58)

B. ship, chin, phone, whale

C. Possible answers:
   **People:** children, father, Phil
   **Animals:** moth, elephant, whale
   **Question words:** when, why
   **Things:** shoe, ship, shower, phone

D. Possible words with digraphs include:
   **-eat:** wheat
   **-in:** chin, thin
   **-en:** when
   **-ine:** shine, thine

E. 1. phone
   2. with
   3. Chin
   4. She

## Lesson 8

### Think About It: Sequence Events (p. 62)

### Practice

A. **4** **Last** Phyllis finished in just over three hours.
   **3** **Then** Phyllis made a strong start in the race.
   **1** **First** Phyllis wanted to run in the Boston Marathon.
   **2** **Second** Phyllis trained hard for the race.

B. **4** **Last** she gets the sleep she needs at night.
   **3** **Then** she jogs or runs.
   **2** **Second** she does warm-up stretches.

### Write About It: Make a List (p. 64)

A. She ran the marathon.
   The party is at Joe's.
   Be there Friday at 7 p.m.

B. Second, when the bell rings, everyone hides.
   Then Joe lets Phyllis in.
   Last everyone jumps out and yells "Surprise!"

### Word Work: Three-letter Initial Blends (p. 66)

B. screw, spray, strawberry
thread, street, three, spring

C. 1. thank
2. sting
3. splash
4. scold

D. Possible words with three-letter blends include:
**-int:** sprint
**-ead:** thread
**-eam:** scream
**-ew:** strew, threw

E. 1. thrill
2. strong
3. sprained
4. spring
5. screamed
6. sprinted

## Lesson 9

### Think About It: Make Inferences (p. 70)

### Practice

1. (1) The boy's dad being at the game was most important.
2. (2) The boy's dad is excited.
3. (2) The boy's hit won the game.
4. (1) The boy's dad was very proud of him.

### Word Work: Three-letter Final Blends (p. 72)

B. fence, hinge, purse, badge

C. 1. lunch
2. bench
3. oranges
4. fudge

E. 1. France
2. purse
3. wedge
4. wrench
5. cringe

## Unit 3 Review (p. 74)

### Reading Review

1. (3) Thrilling moments are an important part of our lives.
2. (2) A stitch in time saves nine.

### Word Work Review

1. thrilling
2. edge
3. scream
4. share
5. phone
6. once
7. three
8. change

# Unit 4 Friendship

## Lesson 10

### Think About It: Understand the Main Idea (p. 78)

### Practice

(3) We all need to share with our friends.

### Word Work: Special Vowel Combinations (p. 80)

B. 1. hawk, dawn
2. voices, spoiled
3. daughter, auto
4. enjoyed, toy

D. 1. sound
2. book
3. looked, room
4. food, house
5. cook, soup, group

## Lesson 11

### Think About It: Find Details (p. 84)

### Practice

C. 1. (1) They may have differences, but the two are best friends.
2. Possible answers: come from different places; different hair; like different things; live with different people
3. Possible answers: know what they want; know where they will go; talk; trust; laugh; know that their friendship will last

### Write About It: Complete a Diagram (p. 86)

B. 1. Flopsy, an English Springer
3. Possible answers: buy food; comb her hair; messy; cleaning up messes; daily walks; warm and cuddly

### Word Work: R-controlled Vowels (p. 88)

B. 1. care
2. share
3. sure
4. admire
5. more

C. 1. close
2. bird
3. clue
4. car
5. cheery

D. Crossword Puzzle

| S | P | E | C | I | A | L | | C | H | O | R | E | S |
|---|---|---|---|---|---|---|---|---|---|---|---|---|---|
| C | | | | | | I | | A | | W | | | H |
| A | D | M | I | R | E | S | | R | U | N | | | O |
| R | | A | | I | | T | | | | | | | R |
| E | | T | | C | | E | | | S | H | A | R | E |
| D | | U | | H | O | N | E | S | T | | | | |
| | | R | | | | | V | | O | | | | |
| | R | E | S | T | O | R | E | | R | I | G | H | T |
| | E | | | E | | | R | | E | | | | R |
| | T | | | R | | | Y | | | | | | U |
| | I | | | R | | | O | | O | | | | S |
| | R | | | O | | | N | | F | | | | T |
| S | E | C | U | R | E | | E | F | F | E | C | T | S |

## Lesson 12

### Think About It: Make Predictions (p. 92)
### Practice

A. 1. (2) She will apply for the job.
   2. (3) He will jump from the plane.

B. Possible answers:
   1. She will win a gold medal with her dive.
   2. The patient will live with a new heart.

### Write About It: Make a Journal Entry (p. 94)

A. 1. I think I will not see her for a long time.

### Word Work: More R-controlled Vowels (p. 96)

A. arm warm marry
   charm quart parent
   part award vary

C. hear wear heard
   appear swear earth
   fear pear learn

## Unit 4 Review (p. 98)

### Reading Review

1. (2) Friends are an important part of our lives.
2. (1) in your family
   (2) neighbors

### Word Work Review

1. care
2. far
3. store
4. very
5. near
6. about
7. four
8. bear

## Writing Skills Mini-Lessons

### Sentences and Capitalization (p. 100)
### Practice

1. **D**on **G**rant wants a better job.
2. **H**e wants to make more money, and so do **I.**
3. **H**ow will **D**on and **I** get new jobs**?**
4. **H**e and **I** will have to work hard to get them.

### Contractions (p. 101)
### Practice

A. 2. don't
   3. isn't
   4. hasn't
   5. couldn't
   6. wouldn't

B. 1. She thinks she can't do it.
   2. Isn't it time for her to try?
   3. She won't give up now.

### Plurals (p. 102)
### Practice

A. 1. cars
   2. classes
   3. parties
   4. benches

B. 1. ideas
   2. workers
   3. bosses
   4. stretches
   5. stories
   6. families

### Adding *-ed* and *-ing* (p. 103)
### Practice

A. 1. retired
   2. wanted
   3. hopped
   4. running
   5. making
   6. buying

B. 1. stopped
   2. smiling
   3. helping
   4. hugged

# Selected Words in *Voyager 1*

able
about
absence
adjourn
admire
advice
afraid
after
again
ahead
air
Alabama
alarm
alike
alive
all
almost
alone
alpha
already
also
always
American
animal
ankle
annoy
another
any
anywhere
appear
apple
apply
appreciate
appreciation
April
arch
argue
arm
arrest
arrive
ask
attention
auto
award
away
awful
back
badge
ball
bare
barren
baseball
bathtub
beach
bear
became
because
bee
been
beet
before
began
behind
being
bell
bench
bent
berry
beside
best
better
bind
bird
bite
black
blame
bleach
bleachers
blessing
blue
board
boat
boil
bold
bone
book
born
boss
bound
box
boy
brace
brain
bran
branch
brass
brave
bravery
bread
break
breakfast
bride
bridge
bright
bring
broil
broke
broken
brook
broom
brother
brown
brush
built
bump
butter
buy
California
call
calm
came
cannot
can't
cape
car
careful
cause
cent
center
ceremony
change
charm
cheat
check
cheer
cherry
chest
child
children
chill
chin
chip
chore
city
clam
clamp
clan
class
claw
clean
clear
clench
clerk
clinch
cling
clip
clock
close
club
clue
clump
coil
cold
college
comb
come
complete
computer
congressman
cook
cool
cost
could
couldn't
country
courage
course
court
courtesy
credit
cried
crock
crowd
crush
cry
cube
cuddly
cure
curiosity
curly
curve
cute
daily
dance
danger
dare
date
daughter
dawn
day
dear
decide
delight
depend
detector
didn't
die
difference
different
dime
dinner
dispute
divide
do
doctor
does
doesn't
done
door
doorway
down
drained
draw
dream
dress
drift
dry
due
duty
dying
each
early
earth
easy
edge
effect
elephant
employ
English
enjoy
error
even
every
everyday
everyone
everywhere
excite
excuse
eye
face
fail
fair
fall
family
far
fare
farm
fast
father
fault
fear
fee
feel
feet
felt
fence
few
field
fifteen
fight
film
finally
find
fine
finish
fire
firefly
first
first-floor
fish
five
flame
flat
flee
fleet
float
flour
flu

fly
foe
folk
fond
food
foot
forever
forget
form
foul
found
four
fourth
Friday
friend
friendship
from
frozen
fudge
fuse
game
garden
gave
GED
generous
Germany
gift
girl
girlfriend
give
glad
gloat
glue
go
goal
goes
gold
good
grab
grace
grad
grain
grand
grandfather
grandmother
grant
grass
greatly
green
grill
grin
grind
groom
ground
group
grow
grub
guest
guy
hair
half
hand
happen
happy
hard
hard-working
haste
hate
have
hawk
head
hear
heard
heart
hedge
held
hello
help
helps
her
here
hero
herself
hide
high
hinge
hire
hoe
hold
home
homework
honest
honesty
honor
hook
hope
hopeful
horse
hour
hourly
house
how
hurt
idea
important
inch
include
instead
into
it's
I've
jail
January
jaw
job
jog
join
journal
journey
joy
jump
June
jungle
just
keen
keep
kill
kind
kite
knew
know
known
lace
lamp
lance
land
language
last
late
laugh
laughter
law
leader
lean
learn
left
less
letter
life
lift
like
line
list
listen
live
look
lose
loud
love
lunch
lunge
made
maid
mail
main
make
many
marathon
mark
marry
mature
may
maybe
mean
medal
merit
merry
menu
mess
messy
Mexico
mice
might
mind
mine
miss
misuse
moment
Monday
money
month
more
most
moth
mother
mourn
move
Mr.
Ms.
much
mule
music
must
my
myself
nail
name
near
neat
need
neighbor
neighborhood
nephew
nerve
nervous
nest
never
new
newspaper
next
nice
night
nine
noise
now
nurse
o'clock
off
oil
OK
old
once
one
opening
orange
other
our
out
outbreak
over
own
paid
pain
parent
part
party
pass
patriot
paw
pay
pear
pearl
peek
peel
penny
people
perfume
peril
period
person
phone
pictures
pinch
pint
place
plan
plane
plant
plate
play
pleat
pledge
plop
plug
plum
plump
point
pool
pour
preach
price
prince
prize
problem
produce
promotion
proud
prove
proverb
pump
pure
purse
put
quail
qualities
quart
question
race
raft
rain

rake
ramp
reach
read
refuse
remember
rent
rescue
rest
restore
retire
rice
rich
ride
right
ring
ripe
road
room
ruby
rule
runner
rust
safe
said
sail
same
sang
save
saw
say
scar
scare
school
scold
scour
scrap
scream
screen
screw
scrub
sea
seat
secure
see
seem
seen
send
sent
series
shade
shake
shale
share
shift
shin
shine
ship
shoe
shone
shop
shore
show
shower
sigh
sight
since
single
sister
six
sky
slap
sleep
slid
slide
slot
smart
smile
smoke
snail
snake
snow
soap
soaring
sold
soldier
some
someday
someone
sometimes
son
soon
sore
sound
soup
sour
space
span
special
spell
spent
spill
spin
spine
splash
splendid
splice
splinter
split
spoil
sprain
spray
spread
spring
sprinkle
sprint
sprout
stamp
stand
star
stare
start
stale
statue
stay
steak
stereo
still
sting
stitch
stole
stool
stop
store
story
straight
strain
strawberry
stray
stream
street
stretch
stride
string
strong
stub
stun
summer
sunny
super
superior
support
sure
surprise
swear
swift
swing
tailor
take
talk
tall
tap
tape
taste
taught
teach
teacher
team
tear
tell
term
terror
test
Texas
than
thank
that
their
them
then
there
these
they
thin
thing
think
this
those
thread
three
threw
thrill
throat
through
throw
Thursday
tight
time
tint
tire
toast
today
toe
together
told
tomorrow
tone
tonight
too
took
tool
tore
town
toy
train
tree
trip
trouble
true
trust
try
tune
Turkey
twice
twinge
two
unfair
union
unit
unite
unsure
until
update
U.S.
use
usually
value
vary
very
visit
voice
wait
wake
walk
want
war
warehouse
warm
waste
watch
wave
way
wear
weed
week
we'll
well
went
we're
were
whale
what
when
where
while
whine
white
who
whole
why
will
window
wing
winner
winter
wish
with
without
woman
won
word
work
world
worm
worth
would
write
wrong
wrote
yeah
year
yell
yesterday
you'll
young
your
yourself
youth
zero

# Writing Skills Rules

## Rules for Writing Sentences

1. A sentence states a complete thought. It begins with a capital letter and ends with a period.
   **I** have a dream.
2. A question begins with a capital letter and ends with a question mark.
   **W**hat is your dream?
3. Always capitalize the word *I*. Capitalize people's names.
   **D**on **G**rant and **I** each have a dream.

## Rules for Contractions

When two words are combined into one and at least one letter is dropped, an apostrophe takes the place of the missing letter.

can not ➡ can't      is not ➡ isn't

## Rules for Adding *-s* or *-es* to Make Words Plural

1. Add *-s* to most words.
   job + s = jobs      game + s = games      day + s = days
2. Add *-es* to words ending in *s*, *x*, *z*, *ch*, and *sh*.
   boss + es = bosses      box + es = boxes      wish + es = wishes
3. If a word ends in a consonant + *y*, change the *y* to *i* and add *-es*.
   city + es = cities      company + es = companies

## Rules for Adding *-ed* and *-ing*

1. Add *-ed* or *-ing* to most words without changing anything.
   warn + ed = warned      warn + ing = warning
2. If a word ends in silent *e*, drop the *e* and add *-ed* or *-ing*.
   hope + ed = hoped      hope + ing = hoping
3. If a word ends with a short vowel followed by a consonant, double the consonant before adding *-ed* or *-ing*.
   plan + ed = planned      plan + ing = planning